Microprocessor Interfacing

Microprocessor Interfacing

Graham Dixey CEng, MIEE

Stanley Thornes (Publishers) Ltd

First published in 1991 by:
Stanley Thornes (Publishers) Ltd
Old Station Drive
Leckhampton
CHELTENHAM GL53 0DN
England

British Library Cataloguing in Publication Data

Dixey, Graham
    Microprocessor interfacing.
    I. Title   II. Thomas, Andy
    004.16

    ISBN 0–7487–0583–X

Typeset by Florencetype Limited.
Printed and bound in Great Britain at The Bath Press, Avon.

Contents

Appendix B

Bibliography

Index

Foreword

In 1982 Hutchinson Educational Publishers, now part of Stanley Thornes, published on behalf of the Business Technician Education Council (BTEC), a series of books designed for use as learning packages in association with the published standard units in Microelectronic Systems and Microprocessor-based Systems.

The last decade has seen the transformation of industrial computing with the explosion in personal computing. The reduction in price complemented by a significant increase in computing power has extended the application of personal computers so that microelectronics is now a realistic tool in all sectors of industry and commerce. The need for adequate training programmes for technicians and engineers has increased and the BTEC units have been revised and updated to reflect today's needs.

Stanley Thornes have produced a series of learning packages to support the updated syllabuses and numerous other courses which include Microelectronics and Microprocessor-based Systems. There are five books in the series:

Microelectronic Systems	Level F	by G. Cornell
Microelectronics NII	Level N	by D. Turner
Microelectronics NIII	Level N	by D. Turner
Microprocessor-Based Systems	Level H	by R. Seals
Microcomputer Systems	Level H	by R. Seals

Two additional books which complement the five above are:

Microprocessor Interfacing	Level N	by G. Dixey
Practical Exercises in Microelectronics	Level N	by D. Turner

Interfacing is an essential, but often neglected, stage in the application of Microprocessors and Microelectronics to any process. This book follows the BTEC unit and supports the first three titles above. Practical Exercises in Microelectronics is a series of exercises which complement the two Microelectronics Level NII and Level NIII books with a programme of relevant laboratory-based exercises.

Andy Thomas
Series Editor

Preface

This book has been written with two objectives in mind. The first was straightforward enough – to cover the syllabus of the Level III BTEC half-unit of *Microprocessor Interfacing* (thus accounting for the title of the book!). The second was to produce, coincidentally, a book that would also be relevant to the needs of a much wider readership. Since this is, by its nature, a somewhat specialised text, it is expected that readers in the latter category will have at least a nodding acquaintance with basic microprocessor principles, as well as a working knowledge of fundamental electronics. With both aims in view, I have attempted to ensure a logical continuity of approach to the subject. This should benefit particularly the reader who starts at the first word and ends with the last. Nonetheless, those who wish to 'dip in here and there' for specific items of information should find their task that much easier.

I hope that this book is both readable and informative, since the acquisition of knowledge, for whatever reason, should never be a chore. Instead, it should lead the reader on to want to know even more.

Graham Dixey   Harrow 1990

ONE

A system overview

The power of the microcomputer is evident to all. Those who use computers a great deal, whether at work or at home, automatically accept the interaction that takes place between human and machine. This interaction is performed through the medium of an *interface*, this being a hardware device, simple or complex, that allows communication between the computer and its *peripherals*, with or without the intervention of a human operator. The word peripheral is a general term, used to describe anything that is connected to the computer but lies outside its periphery. In effect, the peripheral is a necessary feature of the computer's working environment, but is not actually an integral part of the computer itself.

Figure 1.1 is a schematic diagram of a computer connected to a number of peripherals, in a context which most should find familiar. The peripherals shown in this figure are: a Visual Display Unit, or VDU (also known as a monitor); a keyboard; a disk-drive unit (hard or floppy); a printer and a mouse. Figure 1.1 merely shows, in a very general way, how the computer is central to its peripherals. It does not show the interfaces mentioned previously, nor does it indicate what the 'microcomputer' actually comprises.

A brief consideration of the functions of each of the peripherals of Figure 1.1 should make clear that communication takes place between the peripherals and the computer.

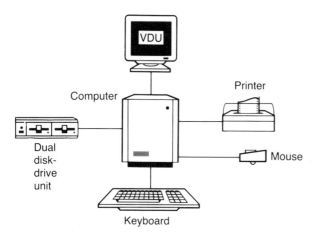

Figure 1.1   A familiar situation in which a computer is working with a number of peripherals

PERIPHERALS

Communication in any context implies the flow of information, of one sort of another, between at least two points. The keyboard allows the computer user to send information (known more succinctly as *data*) to the computer, a character at a time. Pressing a key generates a response that alerts a routine that identifies the key pressed and produces a code corresponding to the character or function of that particular key. The reader may already be familiar with the code most widely used, known as ASCII (American Standard Code for Information Interchange). The *VDU* is a type of display device generally associated with the keyboard, in that when a character key is pressed, that character is 'echoed' to the screen of the VDU to provide visual feedback to the user's actions. The VDU does, of course, have wider use than this, being the usual means by which the computer communicates with the user, whether in the form of text and/or graphics.

The *disk-drive unit* is simply a storage device, usually of very high capacity; it is often referred to as *backing store*. The disks used with these drives may contain commercial software, such as word processors and databases, or user files, often comprising the data generated by the usage of the latter programs. When the user wishes to make use of a disk-drive, access to the storage area on the disk is obtained by means of the operations 'load' (in which the computer receives data from the disk) or 'save' (in which the computer sends data to the disk).

It is difficult to visualise a system such as that in Figure 1.1 operating without a *printer*. This is an essential device for obtaining *hard copy* of the results of computer activity. Communication between computer and printer is essentially 'one way', in that it is the computer that is sending data to the printer. However, in a more limited sense, the printer also communicates with the computer by informing the latter when it is ready to accept more data and when not. This limited communication is associated with a problem discussed in more detail later, namely synchronising the computer's high speed to the very much slower pace of even the fastest printer.

A *mouse* is a popular and useful form of input device, commonly used in what is termed a WIMP environment – Windows Icons Mouse Pointers. Suffice to say that it is yet another means of allowing the user to communicate (strictly one way in this case) with the computer.

THE COMPUTER

The term computer is often used rather loosely and may describe a complete workstation, with keyboard, VDU and printer. In the more specific situation of Figure 1.1, the 'computer' occupies a block of its own and each of the other blocks – keyboard, mouse, dual disk-drive unit, VDU and printer, while essential, are classified as its peripherals. It is necessary, therefore, to look at the computer block in a little more detail in order

to gain a better understanding of its functions. This will then make it easier to put the functions of the various peripherals into context.

Figure 1.2 shows in a generalised form the component parts of a computer. The purpose of each of these will now be briefly described. The use of the word 'generalised' should be noted: it implies a universal idea that can be modified to suit particular circumstances. This is an important concept because it points to one of the most powerful aspects of the modern microcomputer – its flexibility.

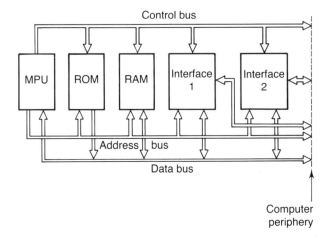

Figure 1.2 The computer block of Figure 1.1 in greater detail, showing the essential structure (architecture) of a typical computer

Figure 1.2 also shows that the microcomputer contains a number of 'blocks', of which the leftmost is marked *MPU*, short for *MicroProcessor Unit*. This block is the 'heart' of the computer. Here the program instructions are decoded and acted upon; here the system timing originates that causes the program to run in the required sequence. The MPU is sometimes referred to as the *CPU*, which stands for *Central Processor Unit*. The alternative term actually means exactly the same thing, but was originally more commonly applied to the larger mini- and mainframe computers. Well-known examples are the 6502, Z80, 8086, 80286 and 68000 microprocessors.

PROGRAMS AND MEMORY

By itself the microprocessor would achieve nothing. To make it do something it must be given a *program*, which is merely a list of instructions which it obeys one by one in a totally slavish manner. This program will normally be stored in part of the *memory* of the computer. The second and third blocks (from the left) in Figure 1.2 show two alternative types of memory, known as *ROM* (Read Only Memory) and *RAM* (Random Access Memory, more usefully thought of as read/write memory). Most computers will have programs stored in both types of memory.

Programs that are stored in ROM often allow the computer to perform a variety of important but quite mundane functions, sometimes known collectively as *housekeeping*. Such programs include routines for reading the keyboard, writing to screen, carrying out diagnostic checks, and so on. Alternatively they may provide specific functions, such as running a high-level language (BASIC, Pascal, etc.) or perhaps word-processing or keeping a spreadsheet, to name just a few of the numerous possibilities. There are other situations, less obvious to the casual observer, where programs are stored in ROM to control some process, whether it is the cycle of a dishwasher or part of the avionics systems of an aeroplane or missile in flight.

The programs that exist in the RAM type of memory will normally be those entered by the user, usually from an external storage device such as a disk-drive, although it is, of course, possible to enter short programs into RAM directly from the keyboard. The amount of RAM available dictates the size of program that can be entered into and run on a given computer. The capacity of memory is measured in *kilobytes*, where *kilo* (K), in computing parlance, is actually 1024 and not the more familiar 1000, and where a *byte* describes a binary number that is generally accepted as being eight *bit*s in length. In turn, and going down the scale to the smallest item of data, the bit is an abbreviation of BInary digiT. Thus, to refer to a computer as having 64K of memory merely means that its RAM has the capacity to store 64×1024, or 65 536 bytes of information, or $65\,536 \times 8 = 524\,288$ bits of data. When it is realised that a single microcomputer instruction may have a length of between one and four bytes, this gives some idea of how large a program may be stored in a given amount of memory.

INTERFACES

The final blocks in Figure 1.2 are the interfaces to the peripherals themselves. Sometimes they are known as the *input/output ports* of the computer, especially when they are provided by a general-purpose interface chip, such as the 6522 VIA (Versatile Interface Adaptor) or the Z80 PIO (Parallel Input/Output). Other interfaces may have names which, by familiarity, determine their likely function. For example, the Centronics parallel port is used with a number of popular printers, whereas some printers either require, or offer the option of, the use of a serial connection such as RS232C. The latter type of interface is also used in communications applications, over the public telephone network.

Connecting all of these blocks are the 'highways' known as *buses*: the *address bus* is used to identify and access the required area of memory at any instant; the *data bus* is used to transfer data back and forth between microprocessor, memory and peripherals; and the *control bus* has functions that include co-ordination of all the events during the running of a computer program.

WHY IS AN INTERFACE NEEDED?

It would be useful to define, in a general way, the function of any interface device. It is not unreasonable to ask why such a device is needed at all. To the initiated it may seem obvious; those with less experience of the ways in which computers and peripherals work may not find it so apparent.

The need for an interface arises either because the signals originating in a peripheral are in some way different from those which the computer requires, or because the signals are of the same type but the speeds at which the computer and peripheral handle the data are quite different. Alternatively, some conversion may be needed just to allow effective communication between the two devices. This reasoning applies whether the data in question is being sent to a peripheral, or being received from one. It may be that the peripheral requires a signal that is quite different from the parallel digital output that the computer normally supplies.

To take each of these points further, one could first of all consider how one signal may actually differ from another.

Types of Signal

All signals may be classified as either *analogue* or *digital*. An analogue signal is one which can take up any of an infinite range of values and is capable of continuous variation within that range. For example, in an audio amplifier the signal could have a value that is anything from a few millivolts to several volts; there is no one level that the signal could be assumed to have. The level of the signal from a moving-coil pick-up, for disk reproduction, would typically be only of the order of 1–2 millivolts. At the other end of the system, where the power is being developed to drive loudspeakers, the signal may be tens of volts in magnitude. The same is true of any system that uses an analogue input and gives an analogue output.

By contrast, a digital signal has only two values, known as *logic 0* and *logic 1*. A system based on these values is termed a *binary system*; this is the system that all digital computers use. It is only necessary to assign nominal values of voltage to these two binary values and to design the computer circuits so that they are capable of distinguishing between them, a quite easy task for them to do. Naturally, if 0 V is assigned to logic 0 and +5 V is assigned to logic 1 (as is quite common), it must be expected that there will be departures from these values due, for example, to voltage drops in the system, but it is quite easy to allow the two logic levels to have reasonable

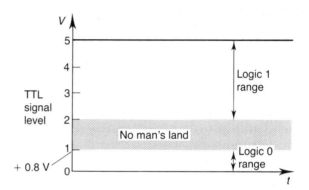

Figure 1.3   Practical limits for TTL logic levels

tolerances and still be capable of being distinguished, one from the other. Figure 1.3 shows commonly accepted limits for the two logic levels, with an area separating them, known rather colourfully as 'no man's land'.

It is now possible to have some idea of the problems that may arise in the design of any microcomputer-controlled system.

DESIGNING A SYSTEM

Suppose some physical quantity, temperature, wind velocity, angular or linear displacement for instance, is being monitored by an analogue device whose output is to be sent to a digital computer for processing. The signal generated by the analogue device and the signal acceptable to the computer are totally incompatible. In all probability the level of the analogue signal is far too small and, since it is an analogue signal, the computer cannot handle it directly anyway. Thus, there are two processes that must be applied to the analogue signal before the computer can accept it.

First, it is necessary to raise the level of the analogue signal – one of the processes known as *conditioning*. Secondly, it is necessary to make an actual conversion from analogue to digital form. The circuit that performs this conversion is known as an *analogue-to-digital converter (ADC)*. This situation arises in many industrial control systems where a computer is used to control a process. This it does by monitoring the variable that is to be controlled (for example furnace temperature) and generating a signal that is sent to a controller to maintain, in this particular instance, the required temperature. This control signal will also often need converting because the controller may well also be an analogue device, quite unable to respond directly to the digital signal produced by the computer. The device that performs this conversion is known as a *digital-to-analogue converter (DAC)*. This situation is shown in a simplified form in Figure 1.4.

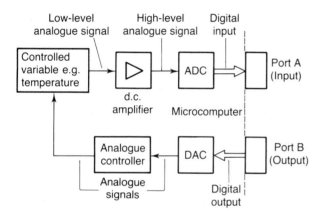

Figure 1.4 A practical control situation involving the conditioning and conversion of analogue and digital signals

The preceding discussion concerned two totally different types of signal. The other possibility mentioned earlier was that the signals were similar but that there was an incompatibility of a different type. This is the case when the computer and a peripheral, both handling digital signals, have quite different operating speeds. A good example of this is when a printer is driven from a computer (a situation touched upon briefly just now). The computer is capable of working at quite incredible speed, often executing thousands of instructions in a few milliseconds. The printer, by contrast, is incredibly slow. Even the fastest printer is virtually at a standstill compared with the speed of the computer. Yet somehow it is essential to synchronise the two so that the printer is kept supplied with data in order that it can carry out its task. An interface is needed that will keep the printer supplied with a stock of data (in an area of memory called a *buffer*), which it can 'top up' from the data held in the computer as required. To do this, the printer and computer will carry out what is called a *handshaking* procedure – a colourful term that describes the way that the printer periodically 'nudges' the computer for more data, through a special control link, so as to keep the printer 'busy'.

Yet another case could also concern a printer but could be equally applicable when connecting a computer into the public telephone network so that it can 'talk' to other computers. The function of the interface now is to convert the normal *parallel* output of the computer into *serial* form. The difference between the two types of digital signal is illustrated in Figure 1.5. The parallel signal needs a separate line for each bit, whereas

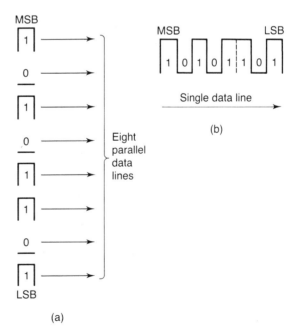

Figure 1.5 The difference between (a) parallel and (b) serial transmission of data. In this example, the data byte being transmitted in both cases is 1 0 1 0 1 1 0 1

only a single line is needed, no matter how many bits the signal has, in the case of serial data. The special advantage of the latter is evident when long-distance communication is the case, although it is obviously a lot slower than parallel transmission because the bits are sent one after the other. Also, extra bits have to be sent to indicate the beginning and end of a data *word*, as well as supplying information that allows errors to be detected and corrected.

Modems, used where communication over telephone lines is required, also have to condition the signal by using it to modulate the telephone carrier – the MO part of MOdem at the sending end – and to demodulate the telephone carrier at the receiving end – the DEM part of moDEM. Figure 1.6 shows two computers communicating through modems. Even here there can be incompatibilities. The rate of transmission and reception of data, known as the *baud rate*, must be the same at both ends of the system, although it does not have to be the same in both directions. For example, if two computers, A and B, are communicating via a serial link, A might transmit to B at, say, 600 baud – in which case B would have to be set to receive at this rate. But B might transmit to A at 2400 baud, in which case A would have to be set to receive at this rate.

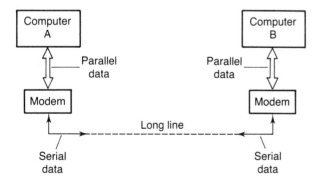

Figure 1.6 Two computers communicating via a telephone line. Both serial–parallel and parallel–serial conversion are involved, as well as MOdulation and DEModulation, hence the term MODEM

In any computer system the 'computer' is the central core. It should be evident by now that the computer consists essentially of the MPU, memory, input/output devices and some additional logic. All of this can be accommodated on a single board, often of quite modest size. In this sense, as mentioned earlier, the VDU, keyboard, disk-drive, etc., are not actually part of the computer proper but are merely peripheral to it. It is quite possible to have a computer without a keyboard, without a VDU or any sophisticated display device and without any external storage device, such as a disk-drive unit. As long as it can run a program and perform some specific task it is still a computer. It will be designed to run a program, stored in ROM, as soon as power is applied to it and any variations on this program can be made by an operator setting some external switches to selected positions. A rather hackneyed, but nonetheless readily appreciated, example is an automatic washing machine. The exact wash program can be predetermined at the start by setting switches and the inbuilt ROM program will look after operations that, in general, are concerned with establishing time durations, water temperatures, switching motors on and off for washing and spinning, and so on.

In this chapter the computer has been seen as the central device to which all other devices are peripheral. The application and way in which certain peripherals communicate with the computer have been described. It was pointed out that a peripheral is connected to the computer through an interface, and some of the possible reasons for requiring such interfaces have been discussed. During the course of this book these important basic ideas will be expanded and the principles and applications of a wide range of interfaces will be discussed in detail. Such a discussion would be meaningless by itself; therefore, space is devoted to a study of how various analogue signals are generated, as well as how such signals are conditioned for acceptance by the computer. Practical applications of interfacing will be described by reference to both the operation of specific peripherals and a case study of a practical situation.

Self-test Questions

1.1 State the processes that must be applied to a low-level analogue signal before it can be processed by a digital computer.

1.2 In what sense is a computer said to 'communicate' with a peripheral? Give two examples of this communication.

1.3 For which of the following peripherals can communication be said to be (a) one way only, (b) two way?

(i) keyboard (ii) visual display unit (iii) disk-drive (iv) mouse

1.4 State *one* advantage and *one* disadvantage of each of (a) parallel transmission of data, (b) serial transmission of data.

1.5 State *one* application of each of (a) read only memory (ROM), (b) random access memory (RAM).

1.6 Draw a block diagram (similar to that of Figure 1.1) for each of the following computer systems:

(a) a wordprocessor

(b) a control system for varying the proportions of chemicals in a three-part mix, the quantity of each individual chemical being determined by opening and closing valves A, B and C.

For each case show only the peripherals relevant to that particular application.

TWO

Transducers

A *transducer* is a device that is able to convert one form of energy into another. It is possible to think of everyday examples where such a conversion occurs, but where a more specific term, rather than the general one of transducer, is used. One such example is the loudspeaker, this being an electro-acoustic device that converts the electrical energy at the output of an amplifier into sound energy. The amplifier in question might be part of an audio system, or a radio or television receiver. The conversion is clearly from an electrical form to a totally different, namely acoustic, one. The microphone is another transducer that performs the opposite process of producing an electrical signal from an acoustic input.

In response to a signal provided by a transducer, it is possible for a computer to exercise a powerful control function over the environment for which the transducer is providing data. In general, therefore, since a computer requires an electrical input, albeit of a particular kind, the transducers of specific interest are those that will convert a wide variety of physical quantities into their electrical equivalents.

In this chapter a wide variety of such devices will be discussed, each capable of converting a particular physical quantity into an electrical signal that the computer is ultimately able to accept and process. The word 'ultimately' is important. Rarely will transducers be found that are able to provide the computer with an input that is directly compatible with its needs. In virtually all cases, the signal will require to undergo the processes of *conditioning* (discussed in Chapter Three) and *conversion* (discussed in Chapter Five).

Examples of the physical quantities that can readily be measured and/or controlled by a computer are: heat, light, weight, force, linear displacement, angular displacement, stress in mechanical structures, fluid velocity, humidity, etc. Indeed, so universal and flexible is the modern digital computer that its applications are really only limited by man's imagination.

Transducers for all of the above quantities exist and more besides. They may all be classified as either *active* or *passive*. To make the distinction clear, an active transducer is one that generates electrical energy directly – a moving-coil microphone is an example, since it uses the principle of electromagnetic induction. By contrast, the passive transducer requires an electrical supply which it then 'modifies' in some way (*modulates*) so as to develop an output. A potentiometer is an example of a passive transducer. It is supplied with a voltage, a proportion of which appears at the wiper according to its position. Thus, the output voltage is directly related to the angular or linear position of the wiper. The latter, in turn, could represent displacement from some given origin.

Transducers for a variety of applications will now be discussed.

TRANSDUCERS FOR TEMPERATURE MEASUREMENT AND CONTROL

The temperature of an industrial oven, furnace or similar environment can be controlled by a microcomputer. Temperatures that may be controlled in this way would probably be classified generally as 'high'. However, there are other examples of controlled temperature environments of a more modest nature. As examples, one could quote biological and botanical applications such as the development of cultures and the propagation of plants. Transducers are available for temperature measurement that develop a voltage proportional to the ambient temperature; others are characterised by a change of resistance that occurs with variation of temperature. Thermocouples are examples of the first type, while resistance thermometers and thermistors represent the latter.

Thermocouples

Thermocouples are temperature-sensitive devices that utilise the Seebeck effect. A thermocouple is formed by joining two dissimilar metals, such that there are two junctions (Figure 2.1(a)). One junction, known as the *hot junction*, is placed at the point where the temperature is to be measured. This junction is a permanent one, usually formed by welding the two metals together. The other junction is known as the *cold junction* since, in use, it lies outside the controlled environment. This junction is closed by a load across which a *thermo-electric* e.m.f. is developed by the flow of thermo-electric current through it; this results from the temperature difference between the hot and cold junctions.

Materials commonly employed for the manufacture of thermocouples include copper/constantan (the latter is a copper/nickel alloy); iron/constantan and nickel chromium/nickel aluminium. Although the basic principles are the same in all cases, the various types will be differentiated by useful temperature ranges and tolerances. Makers' data sheets should be consulted before selecting a thermocouple for any given application. The following abbreviated specification will give an indication of possible characteristics:

In the temperature range

−200 °C to 0 °C: uncalibrated

0 °C to +100 °C: ±1 °C

+100 °C to +400 °C: ±1%

The variation of thermo-electric e.m.f. with temperature for copper/constantan thermocouples is non-linear and, therefore, so is the sensitivity. The latter is expressed in μV/°C, typical figures for temperatures between 0 °C and +400 °C lying in the range 40–60 μV/°C.

For nickel chromium/nickel aluminium thermocouples the relationship between the generated e.m.f. and temperature is linear between at least

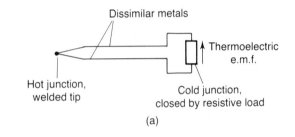

(a)

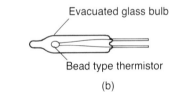

(b)

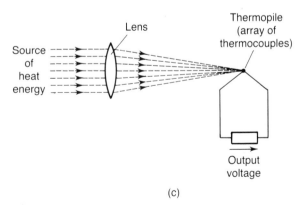

(c)

Figure 2.1 Some transducers for the measurement of temperature: (a) the thermocouple (b) the thermistor and (c) the radiation pyrometer

0 °C and +1000 °C and has a constant sensitivity of 40 μV/°C.

As already stated, the thermo-electric e.m.f. depends upon the difference in temperature between the hot and cold junctions rather than on absolute temperature. The hot junction is in the controlled area while the cold junction is at ambient temperature. Some graphs of e.m.f. versus temperature difference assume that ambient is 0 °C – an unlikely situation for many cases. However, there is likely to be little significant error if such a characteristic is used to deduce the e.m.f. at a given temperature if the difference between this temperature and a more typical ambient temperature of, say, +20 °C is assumed. Thus, using this value of ambient temperature and assuming a controlled temperature of +300 °C, the thermocouple will be subject to a difference of temperature of 300 − 20 = 280 °C. Using this latter value, the graph of Figure 2.2 yields an e.m.f. value of 11.5 mV approximately. This graph is for a particular nickel chromium/nickel aluminium thermocouple. What this graph should make immediately clear is the small voltage that this type of transducer produces. As will be seen in some detail later, this falls well short of the input requirements of the microcomputer and the signal will need to be 'conditioned' before it can be usefully employed as a computer input.

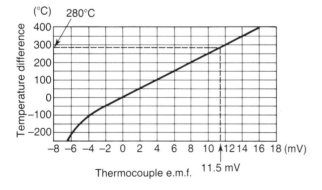

Figure 2.2 Graph of thermocouple e.m.f./temperature for a nickel chromium/nickel aluminium thermocouple

Resistance Thermometers

These operate on the principle that metals change their electrical resistance with changes in temperature. Resistance thermometers are particularly useful where high sensitivity is required. They may be used to measure temperatures from approximately −50 °C to +500 °C. Platinum or nickel are the materials most commonly used.

Taking the specific case of a platinum resistance thermometer, this might have a resistance of 100 ohms at 0 °C. The degree to which resistance varies with temperature is described by the temperature coefficient, whose value in this specific case is taken as 0.385 ohms/°C. This value is found to be constant over the range of −50 °C to +500 °C, owing to the linear nature of the resistance/temperature relationship.

It is necessary to convert this resistance change to a voltage. The usual method of doing this is to include the thermometer in a bridge arrangement. If the bridge is balanced at some reference temperature, any subsequent departure from this temperature will produce a voltage output from the bridge that is proportional to such deviation. Since the thermometer is likely to be situated remotely from the bridge and its instrumentation, lengths of connecting leads will become important and compensation will need to be included. Three alternative bridge arrangements are shown in Figure 2.3. In each case, the output voltage has a slope of 1 mV/°C.

Thermistors

An inexpensive temperature transducer of the resistance thermometer type is the *thermistor* (see Figure 2.1(b)). It is made from sintered mixtures of metal oxides and has semiconductor characteristics. Those used for measurement of temperature (as opposed to detection of temperature change) have a negative temperature coefficient. This means that an increase in temperature causes a reduction in the resistance of the device. The operating temperature is fairly

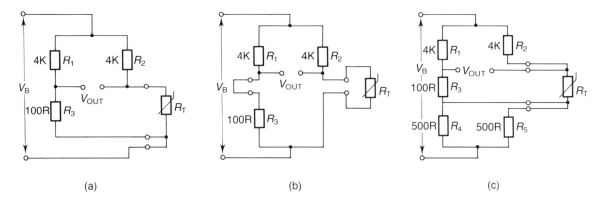

Figure 2.3 Three alternative bridge arrangements for use with resistance thermometers: (a) 3-wire bridge (b) compensating lead bridge (c) Kelvin double bridge

limited ($-100\,°C$ to $+400\,°C$). A typical device might have a resistance of 5000 ohms at $0\,°C$ and 100 ohms at $150\,°C$. One problem with thermistors is the extreme non-linearity of their characteristics but they are very sensitive indeed and, in the bead variety, very fast acting.

The latter variety are usually encapsulated in a small glass bulb, but it is also possible to obtain a purpose-built 'probe', in which the active element is housed in a stainless steel body. A refinement of the latter type is the inclusion of a compression gland that allows the probe to be inserted through the wall of a vessel to measure the temperature of a fluid. The recommended temperature range for one particular probe of this type is from $-10\,°C$ to $+70\,°C$; its resistance at $+50\,°C$ is quoted as being 2000 ohms.

The *radiation pyrometer* of Figure 2.1(c) consists of an assembly of thermocouples that capture heat energy from the source and generate a relatively large voltage. One advantage of this type of transducer is its ability to measure very high temperatures.

Temperature Sensor ICs

Several integrated circuits have been developed specifically for temperature measurement. These provide a linear relation between the temperature sensed and either an output voltage or output current.

The LM35 temperature sensor IC This device, produced by National Semiconductor Corporation, gives a linear output of 10 mV/°C. There are two versions, having different temperature ranges:

LM35DZ $0\,°C$ to $+100\,°C$, with an accuracy at $25\,°C$ of $\pm0.4\,°C$

LM35CZ $-40\,°C$ to $+110\,°C$ with an accuracy at $25\,°C$ of $\pm0.9\,°C$

The encapsulation is a plastic TO92 package, connection details for which are given in Figure 2.4.

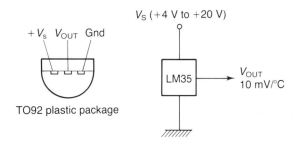

Figure 2.4 The LM35 temperature sensor IC connection details

The 590 kH temperature transducer This device acts as a high impedance, constant current regulator passing $1\,\mu A/K$. It is supplied ready calibrated so that, at $298.2\,K$ ($+25\,°C$), the current

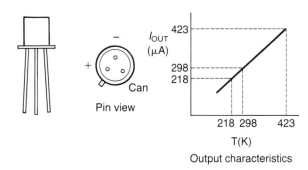

Figure 2.5 The 590 kH temperature transducer

is 298.2 μA ± 2.5 μA. This is a current-sourcing device that is ideally suited to remote sensing over inexpensive *twisted pair* lines. Details are given in Figure 2.5.

TRANSDUCERS FOR FORCE AND DISPLACEMENT

The Strain Gauge

The strain gauge works on the principle that the resistance of a conductor depends upon its physical dimensions. Thus, if there is some external influence that affects any of these dimensions, a change in resistance will occur. This resistance change can be detected and measured in a circuit of the Wheatstone bridge type.

Strain gauges can be of the metallic or semiconductor type. The latter are the more sensitive but suffer from the drawbacks of being less accurate and, as is common with many semiconductor devices, of being somewhat temperature sensitive. The general form of a metallic strain gauge is that it consists of a very fine conductor network that may be unbonded (that is, free in space) or bonded to a fine foil which is itself cemented to the member in which the force is to be measured. Typical resistance values are 120, 350 and 1000 ohms. It is quite usual to place two similar strain gauges in opposite arms of the bridge, one being merely a dummy to give a reference to which the other, under stress, is referred.

By comparison, the semiconductor strain gauge consists of a silicon strip to which ohmic connections are made at the ends.

Both types are shown in Figure 2.6.

Once a strain gauge is bonded to a structural member, it will respond to any dimensional changes in that member. This will, of course, include changes caused by variations in ambient temperature. Errors may occur unless the material of the strain gauge and that of the member in question have similar temperature coefficients of expansion. To avoid this problem 'self-temperature compensated' gauges can be bought that are matched to specific materials, e.g. aluminium and mild steel.

Copper–nickel alloy is commonly used for the construction of strain gauges because of its ability to produce a resistance change that is virtually proportional to the applied strain. This is expressed by the relation:

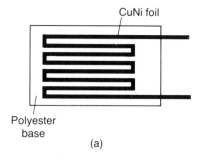

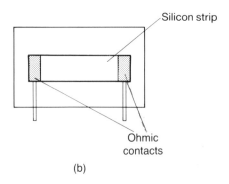

Figure 2.6 Construction of (a) metallic and (b) semiconductor types of strain gauge

$$\frac{\text{Change of resistance } (\delta R)}{\text{Original resistance } (R)} = KE$$

The quantity K is known as the *gauge factor*, while E is the *strain* $(\delta L/L)$. Mathematically:

$$\frac{\delta R}{R} = K\left(\frac{\delta L}{L}\right)$$

whence

$$K = \frac{\delta R/R}{\delta L/L}$$

The above assumes that the applied stress is such that L is the unstressed gauge length and δL is the change due to the applied sress.

Strain gauges are usually connected in a form of bridge circuit, the out-of-balance voltage from which drives the input of a special amplifier. The latter is required because the actual change in resistance is very small, giving rise to a correspondingly small output voltage. For example, a typical change might be 0.2 milli-ohm in 120 ohms per microstrain. When converted, this could well represent a voltage of less than 1 mV! The situation is hardly helped by the possibility that this signal may well 'sit upon' a common-mode voltage of several volts. This latter fact dictates that the amplifier used subsequently to raise the signal level must have exceptional common-mode rejection. In practice one can obtain purpose-built amplifiers having these characteristics.

There is a particular device available that consists of an array of strain gauges, usually four; this is known as a *load cell*. Load cells are used where large forces are to be measured; examples include their use in weighbridges and for measuring the thrust of rocket motors.

The Linear Variable Differential Transformer (LVDT)

This is a transducer that can be used to measure linear displacement directly and, with a simple modification, force as well. The schematic construction is shown in Figure 2.7. A single primary winding is surrounded by two identical secondary windings. A magnetic core, moving along the axis of the coil arrangement, determines the degree of coupling between the primary winding and each secondary winding, according to its position relative to them. If exactly centrally placed, the coupling will be the same to both secondaries and the induced voltages will be equal and opposite. The net output will be zero. Movement in either direction will cause one secondary voltage to be larger than the other; there will then be a net output.

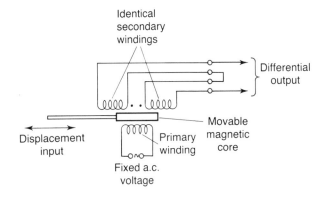

Figure 2.7 Schematic diagram of a linear variable differential transformer (LVDT)

It is not only the magnitude of the displacement that is sensed but the direction also, since there will be a phase reversal as the output signal passes through the null point. This a.c. output can then be applied to a *phase sensitive detector* which will rectify it and develop a d.c. output whose polarity reflects the position of the core within the coil assembly. In other words, as the core moves from one end of the transformer, through centre, to the other, the d.c. output will swing from a large positive value, through zero, to an equally large negative value. This is illustrated in Figure 2.8.

As discussed above, the differential transformer will develop a voltage that is proportional to displacement. It was mentioned earlier that it could also be used to measure force, if modified.

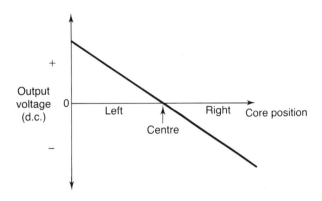

Figure 2.8 Variation of d.c. output with core position for an LVDT used with a phase-sensitive detector

The modification is simple and involves spring-loading the core to its central position. In this way, any movement of the core from this datum will result in an increasing reactive force which the deflecting device must overcome. The further 'off centre' the core is moved, the greater will the deflecting force have to be. Thus, there is a direct relationship between force and linear displacement and, hence, between force and output voltage.

Although obviously a.c. devices, LVDTs requiring only a d.c. supply are also available. They can offer this facility because the necessary electronic circuit is already built in. The circuit consists of an oscillator and phase sensitive detector. These devices appear to offer a compact low-cost solution to the requirement for such transducers. However, their performance is not quite up to the standard of a.c.-only types.

Potentiometric Transducers

Potentiometers, whether linear or rotary, are able to give an output voltage which is a function of the wiper position. Thus, they are useful in providing a *position-dependent voltage*. Various applications may spring to mind, including position feedback in control systems, liquid-level measurement (by using a float and a suitable mechanical linkage to drive the wiper) and input demands from front panel controls. The accuracy of the derived signal depends upon the linearity of the potentiometer track (resistance variation with change of wiper position) and resolution (the number of turns of wire used to make up the track – the finer the wire, the more fragile but the better the resolution).

Both angular and linear potentiometers are available, to give voltages that are proportional to shaft angle or linear displacement, respectively. Potentiometers used for this purpose, while operating on the same principle as the humble radio volume control, are expensive precision devices, characterised by extremely good linearity in the relation between output voltage and shaft movement. To maintain this good linearity, it is essential that no current is drawn from the wiper. Therefore, the output should always be buffered

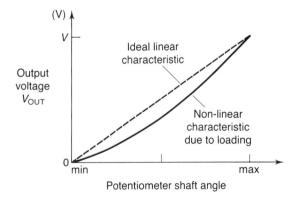
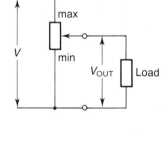

Figure 2.9 Effect of loading on potentiometric transducers

by connection to an amplifier of high input impedance. If this is not done, a loading effect, varying with shaft position, occurs. This is illustrated in Figure 2.9.

TRANSDUCERS FOR THE MEASUREMENT OF FLUID FLOW

Fluids may be either liquids or gases (e.g. air). Several methods exist for measuring the rate of flow, which is normally in an enclosed passage such as a pipe or chamber. Three alternative techniques are shown in Figure 2.10.

In Figure 2.10(a) the fluid flow through a pipe is constricted by an orifice plate. The increase in velocity that occurs as the fluid speeds up to pass through the constriction results in a drop in pressure at the far side. The difference in pressure $(P_1 - P_2)$ is, therefore, a measure of the rate of fluid flow. It does, of course, become necessary to be able to measure the two pressures, requiring yet another transducer(s) for this purpose, so the method is somewhat indirect. Also the measurement is highly non-linear, the flow F being proportional to the square root of the pressure difference.

Figure 2.10(b) shows a specially shaped float that sits in the fluid at a point where the shape of the passage is such that the fluid flow lifts the float. The greater the rate of flow, the higher the float rises in the chamber. A signal output may be obtained either by means of a magnetic follower or by a direct link to the float itself; this may then be used to drive the core of a linear variable differential transformer.

In the method of Figure 2.10(c) the principle is that of a propellor or vane assembly that sits in the fluid flow. The greater the rate of flow, the faster the speed of rotation of the assembly. This speed must then be converted into an electrical signal by a tachometer, for example. The tachometer is often of the pulse type, which makes for easy measurement of rotational speed.

One particular flow sensor provides a pulse output, the frequency of which is proportional to the flow rate. Flow rates from 3–500 litre/hour

can be measured with such devices. A digital equivalent of flow rate can be obtained by gating the pulses into a counter for a fixed 'gate time' and latching the counter output.

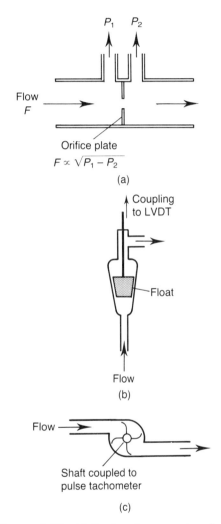

Figure 2.10 Methods of measuring fluid flow: (a) orifice plate, (b) area meter and (c) propellor

MEASUREMENT OF LIQUID LEVEL

Two possible techniques are shown in Figure 2.11. In Figure 2.11(a) a float rests on the liquid surface. Any rise or fall in the liquid level will cause a corresponding movement of the float. If the latter

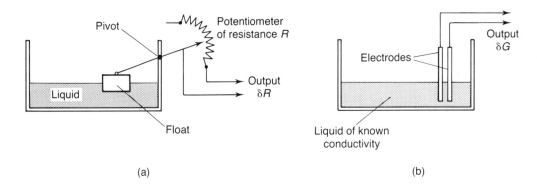

Figure 2.11   Methods of measuring liquid level: (a) the float, (b) the conductivity gauge

can be coupled to a potentiometer, for example, a voltage can be 'picked off' that represents the level of the liquid.

The method of Figure 2.11(b) can be used for liquids whose conductivity is consistent and predictable. A pair of electrodes, connected to some external circuit, are placed vertically in the conducting liquid. The resistance between the electrodes depends upon their area of contact with the liquid. Since this itself depends upon the height of the liquid, any change in the latter produces a corresponding change in the resistance value between the electrodes.

MEASUREMENT OF PRESSURE

Mechanical Transducers

The measurement of pressure may also use mechanical devices whose outputs will require conversion to an electrical signal. Devices are available that use well-established principles; two such possibilities are illustrated in Figure 2.12.

The *Bourdon tube* of Figure 2.12(a) consists of a slightly flattened, coiled metal tube, which is closed at the inner end and open at the other end; the fluid, whose pressure is to be measured, enters the latter end. The natural tendency for the tube, when it is under such pressure, is to try to straighten out. In an earlier age the tube at the centre of the coil was coupled directly to a

pointer that moved over a scale, thus giving an immediate indication of pressure. In modern applications, where an electrical signal is required, this same point must be coupled to a further transducer, such as an LVDT.

Figure 2.12(b) shows another mechanical device, known as a *diaphragm*. This consists of a closed chamber into which the fluid is admitted through an opening at one end. The chamber is sealed by a flexible diaphragm, secured at its periphery, so that its centre can be displaced axially by changes in the applied pressure. Linear movement of the diaphragm can be coupled, as

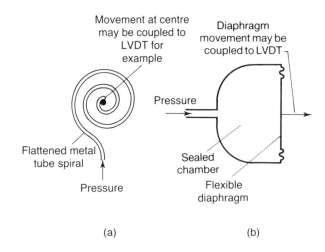

Figure 2.12   Methods of measuring pressure: (a) the Bourdon tube, (b) the diaphragm

mentioned above, to an LVDT to generate the required electrical output. Alternatively, the movement of the diaphragm can be used to actuate a strain gauge element, or even an electromagnetic pick-up.

Piezoelectric Pressure Transducers

The *piezoelectric effect*, in which pressure applied to a crystal generates a voltage, has been used in the past in such applications as the crystal microphone and pick-up. The same principle can be applied to the measurement of pressure, the crystalline material used being silicon. The MPX100AP is an example of such a sensor that provides an accurate, linear output that is related to pressure (or to some degree of vacuum also). Brief details of this device are as follows:

d.c. supply	3–6 V at 6 mA
full-scale span	60 mV
zero pressure offset	20 mV
sensitivity	0.6 mV/kPa
linearity	±0.05% f.s.d.
range	0 to 100 kPa

The style and connections for this particular transducer are shown in Figure 2.13.

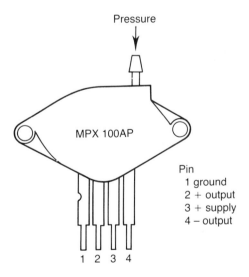

Figure 2.13 The MPX100AP piezoelectric pressure transducer

OPTICAL TRANSDUCERS

The Photoconductive Cell

One of the most useful of optical transducers is the cadmium sulphide (CdS) photoconductive cell. This is a clear plastic case containing a resistance element whose value depends upon the intensity of the light falling on it. Enormous variations in resistance are possible, from tens of kilohms down to a few hundred ohms being typical. The coefficient of resistance change with light level is negative and sufficiently constant to give reasonable linearity between the two quantities.

Optically Coupled Isolators

An optical coupler (Figure 2.14), also known as an *opto-isolator*, consists of a gallium arsenide (GaAs) infra-red emitting diode and a silicon phototransistor mounted in close proximity but electrically isolated. Such a device has the advantages of very high electrical isolation between input and output, good linearity between input and output currents, compatibility with TTL logic circuits, high speed, long life, good mechanical strength and a high current transfer ratio. It can be used as a simple switch or in a linear mode.

In the switching mode the phototransistor operates under saturated conditions and switches between the on and off states. In certain industrial

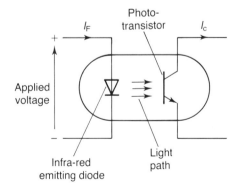

Figure 2.14 An optical coupler or opto-isolator

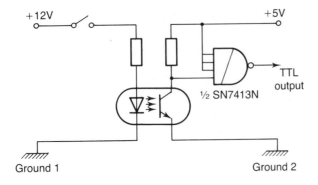

Figure 2.15 An optical coupler arranged to avoid the problems of a noisy environment

applications of digital equipment it is necessary to interface between sensors, such as micro-switches, that are situated in electrically noisy environments, and the control equipment itself. The circuit of Figure 2.15 shows how this can be done with an optical coupler, so avoiding the pick-up of extraneous noise.

The optical coupler can also be used to transmit serial data between two digital systems where there is a substantial difference in the earth line potentials. This is shown in Figure 2.16. The data rate is normally limited to about 125–150 kHz.

Optical couplers also exist as multi-packages, e.g. quad isolators, with high-gain, high-speed circuitry and with triacs as the output switched element.

In the linear mode the linear relationship between diode forward current and phototran-

sistor current is used. In this mode the input current may be a function of some other variable, e.g. resistance change, and the isolator is used purely to obtain linear coupling with a high degree of electrical isolation.

Two other ways of using optical transducers are shown in Figure 2.17. In Figure 2.17(a) an optical coupler is arranged so that a slotted disc passes between the transmitting and receiving sections. Each time the slot appears in the optical path an output pulse is generated. The number of such pulses, from a given instant, is a measure of the number of rotations of the shaft from that instant, while the frequency of the pulses is a measure of the shaft speed. In these ways, the

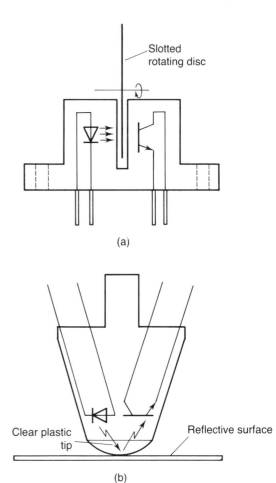

(a)

(b)

Figure 2.17 Two further types of optical transducer: (a) the slotted opto-isolator, (b) reflective transducer

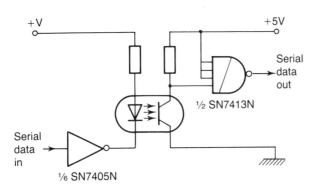

Figure 2.16 An optical coupler used for the transmission of serial digital data

optical coupler can be used as either an event counter or a tachometer.

In Figure 2.17(b) a reflective transducer is shown, which will generate a serial digital output as it moves over a succession of black and white bars (e.g. bar codes). The distance of 5 mm is optimum and can be kept constant by a clear plastic lens at the tip, which contacts the surface.

The Photodiode as an Optical Sensor

The advantage of a photodiode over a CdS cell is its very much faster response, measured in microseconds or even nanoseconds. The silicon photodiode is normally operated with a reverse bias so that in the dark the diode current is extremely small, a few tens of nano-amps only. An increasing light intensity causes a nearly linear increase in diode current. The circuit shown in Figure 2.18 gives an output voltage of 1 V/10 nA of diode current and allows the output to be read by a microcomputer by strobing pin 8 via the 1N914 diode. The low diode currents involved necessitate the use of a CMOS opamp and correspondingly high values of the input and feedback resistors.

There are a variety of other transducers capable of measuring such quantities as the pH factor of liquids, humidity, density, etc. They all have one thing in common; they produce an analogue output. However, there is one type of transducer that is able to produce a digital output directly. It is called a *digital shaft encoder*.

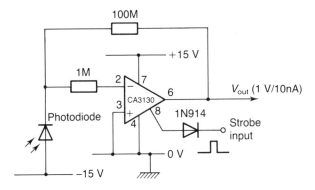

Figure 2.18 Circuit to use a photodiode to measure light intensity

THE DIGITAL SHAFT ENCODER

This is the only true transducer that is capable of giving a parallel digital output. It comprises a circular disk on which a series of radial patterns of light and dark areas, each representing a binary number, is applied, to be read by an array of sensing heads. Each of these binary numbers corresponds to a unique angular position of the disk. Thus, since an 8-bit number can take any of 256 different values, an 8-bit disk (i.e. having eight annular tracks) can identify 256 separate angles, each being $360/256 = 1.4°$ apart. In practice the resolution usually needs to be better than this. The sensing heads may be of the contact, magnetic or optical type.

In the contact type, brushes bear on the annular tracks, either making electrical contact or not according to whether a binary 1 or binary 0 is being read. This type is subject to the usual problems associated with contacts, such as physical wear, dirt, friction, and arcing.

The magnetic type offers an improvement by using a magnetically coated disk on which the binary patterns have been prerecorded. Readout is effected by small toroidally wound heads.

Best of all is the optical type of sensing head. This gives the best accuracy and imposes no mechanical loading on the disk. The disk is usually photo-etched so that it has clear and opaque regions to represent the binary values. The light from a suitable source will then either pass through the disk or not, this being detected by means of photocells. A typical trackwidth is about 12 microns (a micron is a millionth part of a metre) and 14-bit optical encoders are common. With this number of bits the resolution is $2^{14} = 16\,384$ angular intervals, each of value $360/16\,384 = 0.022°$.

The binary pattern used on disk encoders does not follow a pure binary sequence since, if it did, large angular errors would occur whenever the sensors stopped on the junction of two segments. This is because the sense heads always tend to read the *total* number of logical 1 bits and form

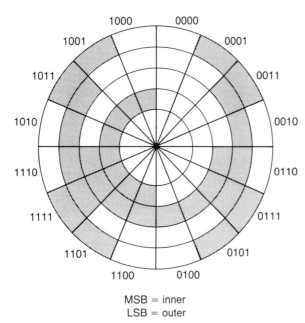

MSB = inner
LSB = outer

Figure 2.19 A 4-bit, Gray-coded, optical shaft encoder disk

the output from this. Thus, a sense head on the junction of 0 1 1 1 (7) and 1 0 0 0 (8) would actually read 1 1 1 1 (15), giving a substantial error. However, if a code is used in which successive binary numbers differ by only a single bit, the error is very small.

Such a code is called a *Gray code*. In this code decimal 7 is 0 1 0 0 and decimal 8 is 1 1 0 0. Sensors bridging the junction of these two numbers would now read 1 1 0 0, thus simply rounding up to the larger value of the two. A 4-bit, Gray-coded, optical shaft encoder disk is shown in Figure 2.19.

SWITCHED INPUTS

Not all inputs to a microcomputer are continuously varying analogue signals. There are many occasions when all that is needed is a simple ON/OFF or YES/NO type of indication. This may represent the limit of some variable, the status of a peripheral, the initiation of an event, etc. In such cases, where the switched input is from a mechanical switch, the arrangement of Figure 2.20 can be used.

A switch is wired in series with a resistor, a value of 1K being typical. With the switch closed, the point A is held at 0 V, i.e. logic 0. The resistor, known as a *pull-up resistor*, plays no part other than drawing an inconsequential 5 mA from the supply. When the switch is now opened, the path to 0 V through the switch is lifted and the point A is 'pulled up' towards +5 V, i.e. logic 1. This type of switched input may be connected directly to a computer input port. The 1K pull-up resistor limits the current into the port to a safe value of no more than 5 mA.

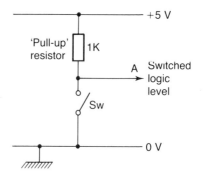

Figure 2.20 Arrangement for a switched logic level input to a computer

Self-test Questions

2.1 Name three transducers that are suitable for the measurement of temperature. In each case state a typical useful temperature range.

2.2 A transducer is required for the measurement of temperature in the range +50 °C to +110 °C. Compare the relative merits of two possible types. From this discussion, make a case for choosing one in preference to the other, stating your own criteria for choice.

2.3 A strain gauge has an unstressed length and resistance of 25 mm and 350 ohms respectively. If the application of stress to the gauge causes an increase in length of 0.2 mm with an accompanying resistance change of 5 ohms, determine:

(a) the gauge factor K

(b) the value of the resulting strain.

2.4 Discuss three applications for optical couplers (opto-isolators).

2.5 What is the reason for using Gray code in connection with digital shaft encoders?

2.6 It is required to measure the linear displacement of a point on a lever in a mechanical coupling. Discuss in detail one way in which a signal could be derived for this purpose.

2.7 Draw a block diagram for a system for measuring:

(a) the rate of flow of liquid through a cylinder

(b) the liquid pressure in the cylinder.

Specify and show the transducers required for both types of measurement in order to obtain two separate electrical signals representing the quantities concerned.

2.8 A 10K potentiometer is supplied with a d.c. voltage between its ends of value 15 V. A 22K resistor is connected between the wiper and the 0 V end. Plot a graph of the voltage between the wiper and the 0 V end, as a function of wiper position, as the wiper is rotated from one end to the other. Hence, deduce the reason for buffering the output of potentiometers used as transducers.

THREE

Signal conditioning

It has already been seen in the previous chapter that the output from many transducers is quite small in value. There may also be certain other undesirable characteristics. For example, the signal may have a d.c. level that 'offsets' its value from that which correctly relates to the magnitude of the physical quantity transduced. An example is where the output from the transducer has a finite value when the variable itself is zero. There may be a non-linear relationship between the transducer output and the measured variable. There may be an unacceptable level of noise present with the required signal. The process of reducing such effects to insignificant proportions is known by the general title of *signal conditioning*.

SCALING: SIGNAL AMPLIFICATION OR ATTENUATION

This conditioning process modifies the analogue signal from the transducer, prior to the analogue-to-digital conversion process (Figure 3.1). A highly desirable end product of conditioning is that the likely range of the analogue signal will now fairly closely match the input voltage range of the converter. This will ensure the best possible resolution being obtained. In the majority of cases, this will mean signal amplification. Specifying the amplifier to be used will mean considering the following criteria.

(a) What output voltage from the transducer corresponds to the maximum value of the input variable?

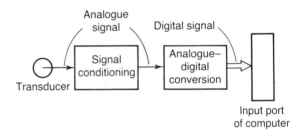

Figure 3.1 Conditioning of an analogue signal is carried out prior to conversion

(b) What is the normal input voltage range for the analogue-to-digital converter chosen, corresponding to full-scale digital output from the converter?

From this data the gain required for the conditioning amplifier can be specified. For example, if the transducer output voltage for the full range of the transduced variable will never exceed 0.1 V, and the analogue input voltage to the converter for full-scale digital output is $+10$ V, then the gain required is given by:

$$\text{Gain} = \frac{\text{Maximum converter input}}{\text{Maximum transducer output}}$$
$$= \frac{10}{0.1}$$
$$= 100$$

HANDLING OFFSETS

When an operational amplifier is used, as is often the case, the elimination of offset in the analogue

22

signal is easily handled. It can be balanced out in exactly the same way as an offset originating in the amplifier itself. The ease arises because such amplifiers invariably include an *offset null* facility. This usually involves connecting a preset potentiometer between two pins of the IC, provided for this specific function. The wiper is often then connected to the negative supply rail. See Figure 3.2(a).

Where such a facility does not exist it is quite easy to provide it. A preset potentiometer is wired between the positive and negative supply rails. The wiper of this control is connected through a resistor of moderately high value to the inverting input (Figure 3.2(b)). If the wiper is first set to the mid-point of the track, with a voltmeter at the amplifier output, the control can be slowly rotated

in the appropriate direction so as to reduce the voltmeter reading (output offset) to zero. This must be carried out with the transducer output (real or simulated) set at the reference value.

It might well be more convenient to simulate the offset voltage from the transducer. This can be done quite easily, provided that its value is accurately known. In Figure 3.2(c), a simple test set-up is shown in which the offset is established using a preset potentiometer RV_1 across the output of a stabilised power supply. A digital voltmeter is used to adjust the offset value to the known value, while a second meter is used to determine the null point as RV_2 is adjusted. The only reason for using RV_1 is to allow fine control of the voltage developed at the wiper, since many power supplies do not allow such precision of setting.

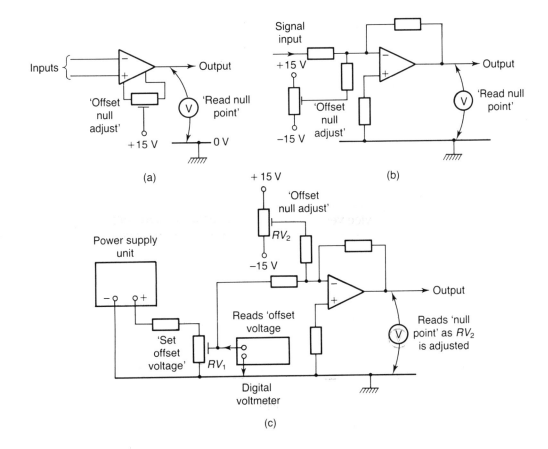

Figure 3.2 Reducing the effect of offsets in the analogue signal: (a) opamp with built-in offset null facility, (b) adding an offset null control to an opamp, (c) simulating the offset voltage for setting-up purposes

REDUCING NOISE LEVELS

When the transducer is situated at some distance from the main computer, as it may well be in some instrumentation applications, the connection from transducer to amplifier should be made using a twisted pair cable. If this cable lies in the magnetic field of some source of interference, any voltages induced in the conductors by this field will have the same amplitude and phase in both of them. Such voltages are known as *common-mode* voltages. If an amplifier of the differential type is used this should have, by design, high inherent common-mode rejection. This is another factor in favour of the use of an operational amplifier for signal conditioning. See Figure 3.3.

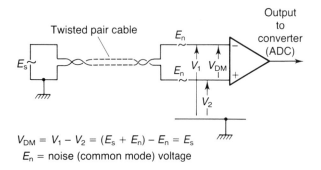

$$V_{DM} = V_1 - V_2 = (E_s + E_n) - E_n = E_s$$
$$E_n = \text{noise (common mode) voltage}$$

Figure 3.3 Remote transducer using twisted pair cable to transmit an analogue signal to a differential amplifier

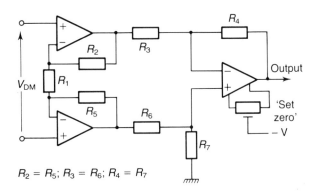

$$R_2 = R_5; \ R_3 = R_6; \ R_4 = R_7$$

Figure 3.4 A common form of instrumentation amplifier

Figure 3.4 shows a possible circuit for an instrumentation amplifier that will provide the required characteristics, as discussed in the preceding sections. It is a differential amplifier with very high gain to differential-mode signals and very low gain to common-mode voltages. As will be seen shortly, the gain can be adjusted over a very wide range. Furthermore, adjustment of the final amplifier's 'set-zero' control can be used to balance out any offset voltage present in the analogue input, as discussed earlier. It is also characterised by a very high value of input impedance and a low value of output impedance.

The differential-mode gain, A_{DM}, is given by:

$$A_{DM} = -\left(1 + \frac{2R_2}{R_1}\right)\left(\frac{R_4}{R_3}\right) \qquad [3.1]$$

It will be noted, from Figure 3.4, that resistors R_2–R_7 inclusive are in pairs and these pairs should be matched in value as closely as possible. For this reason, it is usual to select the value of R_1 in order to obtain the required gain. A gain range between unity and 10 000 is possible with this circuit. A possible approach to the design of such an amplifier, to meet a specified gain value, will now be given.

EXAMPLE

If a differential mode gain of 1000 is required, then a choice for the ratio R_4/R_3 could be made as a starting point. If a moderately high ratio is chosen, this will allow a similarly moderate ratio to be used for the term R_2/R_1

Solution

If $R_4 = 100K$ and $R_3 = 4.7K$, this gives a ratio of slightly less than 20 (it is not necessary to calculate its exact value). This shows that the term $[1 + 2(R_2/R_1)]$ will approximate to 50, in order to give the desired gain of 1000.

Since $2(R_2/R_1) \gg 1$, then $2(R_2/R_1) = 50$ (approx.) and $R_2/R_1 = 25$. Choosing a pair of preferred values, say $R_2 = 47K$ and $R_1 = 1.8K$, gives an approximation to the required ratio of 25, namely 26.11.

At this stage, the values determined above should be substituted into equation 3.1. The result is then compared with the design figure of A_{DM} (1000) in order to see how close it is. It is found that, using these particular resistor values, the value of A_{DM} is 1133 approximately, rather higher than required.

Since R_1 is to be the variable, this value should be increased and a new value of gain calculated. Choosing the new value of R_1 as 2.2K will give a revised gain figure of 930. Clearly, since this is too low, the actual value of R_1 to give a gain of exactly 1000 will lie between 1.8K and 2.2K. In practice a fixed resistor of value, say, 1.8K in series with a 470 ohm preset potentiometer could be used.

The range of R_1 using this arrangement (and ignoring component tolerances) is from 1.8K to 2.27K. Thus, one has the assurance that the correct gain figure will be obtained, in all probability when the wiper is at about the mid-track position.

It will be remembered that the gain, as defined by equation 3.1, had a negative sign. This implies a phase reversal of the signal between input and output of the amplifier. Should this not be desirable, it can be eliminated by exchanging the + and − input connections on the final opamp IC3.

This example is included to show how a simple, pragmatic approach will yield a sensible, easily engineered solution to this type of circuit design problem.

Programmable Instrumentation Amplifier

It is possible to obtain an integrated circuit amplifier in which digitally controlled electronic switches are used to select various resistor combinations within the module. This gives a range of discrete values for the differential-mode gain, which varies in steps of one from unity to 1024. By using an amplifier of this type a great deal of flexibility is obtained, since the gain can be determined from within the control program.

ISOLATION AMPLIFIERS

There are certain situations that require a high degree of electrical isolation between the transducer and the computer system itself. This is especially true in medical instrumentation, where the transducer may be in direct contact with a patient's body.

The isolation can be introduced after the signal amplifier. This isolation will take two forms: the isolation of the amplifier power supplies, and the isolation of the signal itself. The former is straightforward and achieved by standard practice, that is, by the inclusion of a double-wound mains transformer. The latter isolation, that of the signal itself, can be achieved by one of two possible methods:

(a) A modulator–transformer–demodulator link.
(b) An opto-isolator, used in the linear mode.

These two techniques are illustrated in Figure 3.5.

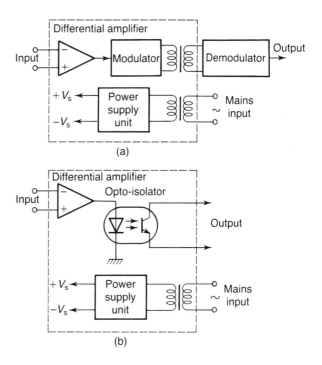

Figure 3.5 Two possible methods of isolating the input signal: (a) by the use of a modulator–transformer–demodulator link, (b) by using an opto-isolator as a linear device

Of the two methods, (b) is the easier to implement. The opto-isolator is able to operate in either a switching mode (such as when it is handling binary signals) or in a linear mode. The latter is possible because there is a linear relationship between the diode forward current and the collector current of the phototransistor.

CONDITIONING AT THE OUTPUT

The reasons for conditioning the analogue signal prior to conversion have already been discussed. In a control system the loop will usually be closed by an analogue controller, which may have been designed for the specific application. Between the computer's output port and this controller a DAC is used for the required digital–analogue

conversion. The full-scale output from this converter will be an analogue signal of substantial amplitude, typically +5 V to +10 V. It is not difficult to take advantage of this large signal availability in a typical control application. Therefore, there would not seem to be much of a case for conditioning of output signals. However, there are one or two special cases that are worthy of discussion.

The first case is illustrated in Figure 3.6, where diagram (a) shows the effect and diagram (b), the cure. The effect is a possible offset at the output of a DAC. Such an offset arises when a zero binary input does not produce a corresponding zero analogue output. If the output of the DAC is coupled to an opamp connected as a non-inverting amplifier, two benefits are possible.

(a) Some additional voltage gain is obtained, this being equal to $1 + (R_1/R_2)$; some impedance buffering accompanies this as an extra benefit.
(b) The 'offset null' control of the opamp can be used to cancel out the offset voltage at the output of the DAC.

The second case relates to the fact that an analogue signal may be classified as being either *unipolar* or *bipolar*. These two types of signal are shown in Figure 3.7 and the difference is immediately evident. The unipolar signal is one that is confined to one polarity only. Although a positive polarity is shown in Figure 3.7(a), an entirely negative signal would also be unipolar, of course. By comparison, a bipolar signal is one that is at some times positive and at other times negative. Regularly recurring

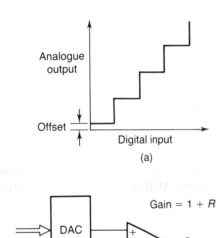

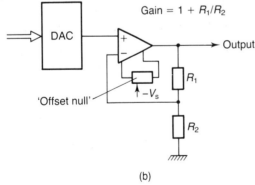

Figure 3.6 Nulling the offset voltage at the output of a DAC: (a) the effect of offset on the analogue output, (b) use of amplifier 'offset null' control to eliminate the offset voltage

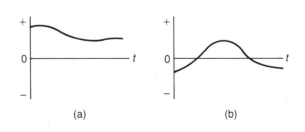

Figure 3.7 Examples of (a) a unipolar signal (b) a bipolar signal

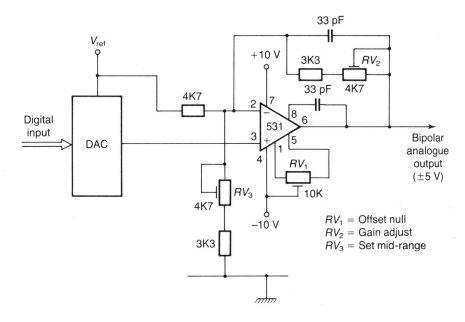

Figure 3.8 Method of obtaining a bipolar output voltage from a DAC

waveforms, such as sine waves and square waves are examples of bipolar signals. However, in the case of a control system, a bipolar output does not necessarily mean a regular waveform at all; it might simply be that the analogue output is required to be either positive or negative at different times, according to the demands of system operation.

This type of requirement obviously raises particular problems, since a DAC normally outputs a unipolar signal in response to a certain binary input range. To convert this to a bipolar signal means making the mid-range binary value equate to zero (assuming a symmetrical output is what is wanted); the maximum binary value then corresponds to the largest positive analogue value, while zero binary signal corresponds to the largest negative analogue voltage. Such a system is said to use an *offset binary* code. The arrangement of Figure 3.8 will effect the required conversion.

The 531 operational amplifier is effectively wired as a non-inverting amplifier whose gain is preset to the required value by adjustment of RV_2. Without the connection from the DAC's reference

voltage V_{ref}, via the 4.7K resistor, to the amplifier's inverting input, the output would be a unipolar analogue voltage. However, with this connection a bias equal to the Most Significant Bit (MSB) of the binary value has been applied to the amplifier's inverting input. Thus, only those binary inputs whose values exceed the MSB will produce a positive output. Those binary inputs less than the MSB will produce negative outputs, while a binary value equal to the MSB will produce zero output. For an 8-bit converter, with a full 10 V analogue swing at the output, the following will be true:

the binary values 0 0 0 0 0 0 0 0 – 0 1 1 1 1 1 1 1

will produce −5 V to 0 V

1 0 0 0 0 0 0 0

will produce zero volts

1 0 0 0 0 0 0 1 – 1 1 1 1 1 1 1 1

will produce 0 V to +5 V

(The analogue ranges quoted are approximate.)

The preset resistor RV_3 is used to adjust the mid-range value for zero volts output. Obviously the setting of RV_2 will interact with that of RV_3 to some extent, so alternate adjustment of each will be required. Preset resistor RV_1 is used to zero the amplifier output when the binary input to the converter is zero. This is the normal offset null control.

One application that a circuit of this type is suitable for is the generation of true alternating signals. Thus, it is possible to generate sine waves, for example, over a wide range of frequencies.

Self-test Questions

3.1 State *three* possible reasons why the output of a transducer might need conditioning prior to conversion.

3.2 Discuss what is meant by scaling a signal.

3.3 Draw diagrams to show *two* ways in which signal offset may be eliminated.

3.4 Assume that a transducer output requires amplification 400 times. Using a differential amplifier as a basis, draw the diagram of, and calculate possible component values for, a suitable circuit.
It is suggested that the design example given in the text is followed for guidance.

3.5 How can electrical isolation of a transducer signal be achieved? Give an example where such isolation would be essential.

3.6 Differentiate between unipolar and bipolar signals. How is it possible to convert a unipolar signal to a bipolar one?

FOUR

Time and code conversions

CODE CONVERSIONS

Conditioning has been seen as a means of overcoming some of the incompatibilities between the signal that a transducer develops and the input that an analogue-to-digital converter requires. The latter performs what is, in effect, a code conversion. The term code here is used in a very general sense to indicate the *form* of a signal. In a more specific sense, it could mean a particular type of digital code, such as pure binary code, 8421 BCD code, or Gray code. The code conversion normally carried out by an analogue-to-digital converter is from analogue to pure binary. This subject is covered extensively in the next chapter, so no more need be said here. As far as inputs to the computer are concerned, most code conversions will be of this type. However, it was seen in Chapter Two that there is one transducer that produces a type of binary code directly. This device is the *disk encoder*, and the code that it produces is called *Gray code*. This can be converted to pure binary code by the method shown in Figure 4.1.

This figure shows a disk encoder producing an *n*-bit parallel Gray-coded output. When an angular position is read by the array of optical sensors, the individual bits of the data word are clocked in serially to one of the inputs of a 2-input AND gate. The output of this gate drives the clock input of a toggle-type flip-flop. This may well be a JK flip-flop wired in the toggle mode, by connecting its J and K terminals to logic 1 (+5 V). It is characteristic of this type of flip-flop that a change of state only takes place when the clock input goes from logic 1 to logic 0 (a negative-going transition). A positive transition produces no effect. This is the basis of the conversion method, which works as follows. Consider the conversion of a 4-bit Gray-coded word into pure binary. As an example, assume that the flip-flop is initially cleared (Q = 0) and that the Gray code input is 1 1 1 1. The fact that there are four discrete pulses (see Figure 4.2) means that there will be four negative transitions, one at the trailing edge

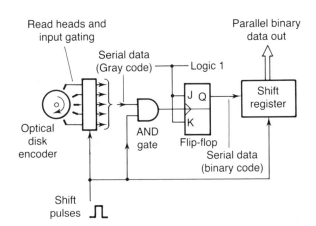

Figure 4.1 System for converting Gray code to pure binary

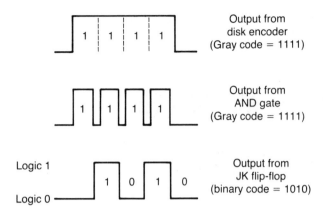

Figure 4.2 Converting the Gray code value 1 1 1 1 to its pure binary code equivalent (1 0 1 0)

of each pulse. Hence, the flip-flop will change state four times. If Q starts off at logic 0 then, after the first clock pulse, it will have changed to logic 1, after the second clock pulse it will be logic 0 again, after the third clock pulse it will change to logic 1 and, finally, after the fourth clock pulse, Q will return to logic 0. A Gray code input of 1 1 1 1 (denary 10) will have produced a pure binary output of 1 0 1 0 (also denary 10, of course). The reader is invited to try other Gray code values; in all cases, they will be found to produce the equivalent binary value.

Figure 4.1 also shows that the serial output of the flip-flop is converted to parallel form by means of a *serial-in, parallel-out* shift register. This is clocked from the same source that is used both to clock in data from the optical disk and to enable the AND gate. It might be wondered why the AND gate is needed at all. It is vital to the operation, since it ensures that the clock input to the flip-flop consists of discrete pulses. For example, if the data from the disk contained two or more consecutive logic 1s, these would normally be seen as a continuous logic 1 level occupying the time equivalent of these pulses. The flip-flop would, accordingly, only change state at the end of the sequence of 1s rather than at the end of each individual pulse time interval. The application of an external clock pulse to one

input of the AND gate forces the output of the gate (and hence the clock input of the flip-flop) to return momentarily to logic 0 between clock pulses.

TIME CONVERSIONS

The speed of execution of a microcomputer program is incredibly fast. Even the older, somewhat slower, 8-bit microprocessors take only a few microseconds to carry out each instruction. Therefore, a program with, say, a thousand such instructions could well run in a mere 5 ms! Naturally, there are going to be situations where even this speed is inadequate. However, what needs to be considered now is what should be done when the peripheral connected to the computer is very much slower. Somehow the two different speeds have to be synchronised. In effect a time conversion is carried out. The term applied to this is *handshaking*.

Handshaking

To use a handshaking technique, the computer and peripheral are connected together by appropriate control lines, either two or three in number; they are also linked by the data bus, on which the actual transfer of data will be made (see Figure 4.3). The control lines are known as the handshaking lines. Where only two such lines

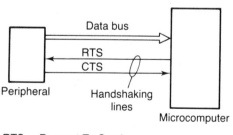

RTS = Request To Send
CTS = Clear To Send

Figure 4.3 Computer and peripheral communicating with handshake lines (RTS–Request To Send; CTS–Clear To Send)

are used, one is employed by the sending end to 'request' the receiving end to accept fresh data. The other line is used by the receiving end to respond to this request. In the event that the receiving device is not ready for new data, it is said to be 'busy'. This state will be indicated by the logic level on the handshaking line just referred to. The names given to these lines will vary somewhat between one situation and another, but their meaning should always be clear. For example, the label RTS (Request To Send) might apply to one line, while the response could be made on a line labelled CTS (Clear To Send).

Handshaking can be used at either input or output of a computer. Taking an example of input handshaking, an Analogue-to-Digital Converter (ADC) requires a finite time to carry out a signal conversion. In such a situation, the computer needs to know when the conversion cycle is complete. One handshaking line will be used to inform the computer of this event. At the time that this line is activated the data on the data bus will be known to be correct (valid) and the microcomputer will accept it. A second handshaking line will be used for the computer to 'tell' the converter to start another conversion cycle. This sequence of events can be understood by referring to the flowchart of Figure 4.4 and the timing diagram of Figure 4.5.

In the first block of the flowchart the conversion process is initiated by the computer sending a Start Convert pulse to the ADC on one handshaking line. The program then loops and periodically checks the other handshake line (known as Status) to find out when the conversion is complete. This latter line will change logic level at this time, this being detected by the program. The program will exit from the loop and the data will be read through the computer's input port. After this, the program will jump back to the start to initiate a new conversion cycle. The process repeats indefinitely. The handshaking program may be thought of as having three parts, corresponding to the three blocks of the flowchart of Figure 4.4.

Referring to the timing diagram of Figure 4.5, at an instant of time, denoted by t_0, the Start Convert

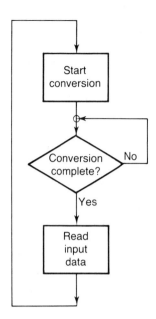

Figure 4.4 Flowchart for handshaking

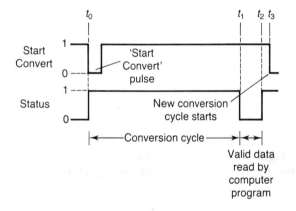

Figure 4.5 Timing diagram for handshaking during an analogue-to-digital conversion

line from the computer to the ADC is momentarily taken low. It is from this point in time that the conversion process starts. When the conversion process is complete, the Status line from ADC to computer goes low to tell the computer that the data at the output of the ADC is now valid; this is instant t_1. Between this instant and a further point in time, denoted as t_2, the computer program reads in the data at the input port (from the ADC).

The process repeats when a new Start Convert pulse is issued at time t_3.

An example of handshaking at the output can be seen in the supply of data to a printer. It will be necessary to include in the printer interface some handshaking lines so that the comparatively slow electromechanical printer is able to tell the computer when it needs fresh data. A popular printer interface is the Centronics interface. This is discussed further in Chapter Eight.

A further discussion of handshaking will be found in Chapter Five, where converters and their applications are dealt with.

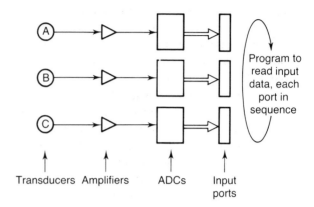

Figure 4.6 Multiple input system with independent hardware for each channel

SYSTEMS WITH MULTIPLE INPUTS

While some control systems require only a single transducer to provide the input data, there are systems which need several, or even many, separate inputs. These may take the form of continuously varying voltages from transducers of the type described in Chapter Two; alternatively, they may be simple switched inputs, providing only an ON/OFF indication of some state. Either way, it is evident that provision must be made for handling these multiple inputs in an organised fashion. In general, it is not feasible to accept data from all inputs simultaneously, so some form of time-sharing has to be provided.

It will be necessary to study the problem from two points of view. One of these is the hardware aspect; the other factor that will need to be considered is the software to handle the input data.

An easy way of organising the hardware is to provide a completely independent signal path for each input. For the case of three signals, for example, the hardware would involve a simple triplication. Figure 4.6 shows a system such as this, in which three transducers, A, B and C have their own amplifiers, converters and input ports. What is still common to all three inputs is the program that reads the data at each of these ports. This is the software aspect mentioned. This could be implemented by the simple expedient of writing a loop that continuously reads the data at each port in turn. How often this needs to be done depends upon the rate at which the analogue signal varies. The slower the variation, the less often does the data need to be read. Another factor to be considered is the speed of conversion. As just mentioned, and as discussed further in the next chapter, it is usual to operate a handshaking procedure between a converter and the computer, so that the latter only attempts to read the data input when the converter tells it that the conversion cycle is complete. This obviously creates additional complication when there are several converters working at once. The conversion times may be different at different times, depending upon the type of converter used.

MULTIPLEXED INPUTS

Apart from the complications mentioned above, systems organised along these lines are going to use rather a lot of hardware. One therefore needs to consider whether there is another way in which multiple inputs can be handled. The answer is to use *multiplexing*. When this approach is adopted, the inputs are accepted in sequence, with at least some of the hardware common to several or all input lines.

In Figure 4.7 the three transducers of Figure 4.6

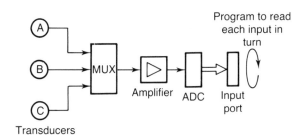

Figure 4.7 Multiplexing all three inputs of Figure 4.6 on to a common channel

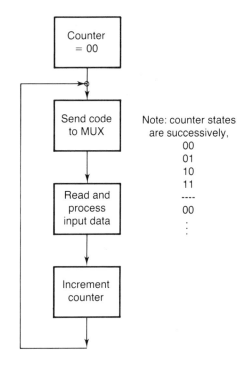

Figure 4.8 Flowchart for multiplexing and demultiplexing four separate transducer inputs

are shown connected to the input of a block marked MUX (the standard abbreviation for MUltipleXer, commonly used on system diagrams). The function of the multiplexer is to select each of the inputs in sequence: A,B,C,A,B, ... and pass each signal in turn on to the amplifier. From then on the path is common to all inputs. The multiplexer behaves rather like a high-speed electronic rotary selector switch. From this it is obvious that each signal is being 'looked at' for a short, specific interval of time. This system is, in fact, known more fully as *time-division multiplexing* since each signal is allocated its own 'slot' in time.

The opposite of multiplexing is, logically, known as *demultiplexing* and the device that performs this function is called a demultiplexer or DEMUX, to use the usual abbreviation. In terms of hardware, there is a specific device that fulfils this function. However, in the case of the type of system being described, there may not be an actual block bearing this label. Certainly there is no evidence of one in Figure 4.7. The secret, if it can be called that, is to let the computer run a program that effectively performs the demultiplexing function itself. After all, the computer must read the input data in order to make any use of it at all. All that it is necessary to do, is to make sure that when the appropriate transducer is 'on line', the program segment that handles the digital quantity corresponding to that transducer's output is the one that is called. Thus, for each input from A, B and C, there exists a short section of program that is run when that particular

transducer is the one selected by the multiplexer.

This calls for some form of synchronisation between the MUX block and the program itself. One way of achieving this is to make the program itself generate the codes that perform the multiplexing sequence. All this sounds more complex than it really is. For a multiplexer handling four inputs, the sequence is achieved by cycling through the codes 00, 01, 10 and 11 on the control inputs. Such a sequence is readily generated by software. The flowchart of Figure 4.8 shows how this works.

First the program sends the code 00 to the MUX block; this selects transducer A, so the program segment that runs now reads the data from this input into the computer. At the conclusion of this operation, the next code, namely 01, is used to select transducer B. The program segment for this input is now run. This is followed by code 10, and the program segment to read in from transducer C, followed finally by the code 11 and the program that reads in data from transducer D. After this point, the sequence merely repeats itself.

The above has discussed briefly the basic idea of multiplexing and demultiplexing in the particular context of multiple inputs. This should have made the saving of hardware an obvious advantage of the method. The system of Figure 4.7 uses three blocks only: MUX, amplifier and ADC. It is based on a particular assumption that may not always be true. That assumption is that the gain of the amplifier will be correct for all three inputs. The purpose of the amplifier will be recalled from the relevant discussions in Chapter Three. The amplifier raises the signal level to match the full-scale input of the converter, in order to obtain full benefit from the available resolution. If the amplifier gain is unsuitable, two possible effects will occur:

(a) If the gain is too low, the maximum analogue input will not produce maximum digital output. The best possible resolution will not be achieved.

(b) If the gain is too high, the converter will produce its maximum digital output at an analogue level less than maximum. The output from the converter will saturate at this lower level. Values of analogue voltage above this level will clearly be in error.

Minor variations in the gain requirement may not matter, especially if there is a substantial hardware saving. Under such circumstances it is vital that the gain is determined for the highest level of analogue input, in order that the gain for any input is not too high.

EXAMPLE
Three transducers, A, B and C develop analogue voltages corresponding to the maximum values of the three input variables as follows: $A = 10\,\text{mV}$, $B = 15\,\text{mV}$ and $C = 18\,\text{mV}$. If the converter to be used has a full-scale input range of $+10\,\text{V}$, calculate a suitable value of amplifier gain for a multiplexed input system. Comment upon the resolution of each input.

Solution
The amplifier gain A_v is determined by considering how much the largest analogue input must be amplified in order to develop the full-scale input to the converter. That is, amplifier gain is given by:

$$A_v = \frac{\text{Full-scale converter input}}{\text{Maximum transducer output}}$$

$$= \frac{10}{18 \times 10^{-3}}$$

$$= 555.56$$

This will give the maximum resolution for this input (transducer C).

For transducer A, the input is only 10 mV and the resolution will be reduced in the ratio of $^{10}/_{18} = 0.56$ of the maximum resolution possible.

For transducer B, where the input is 15 mV, the resolution will be reduced in the ratio of $^{15}/_{18} = 0.83$ of the maximum resolution possible.

If the signal variation is too great to allow a common amplifier to be used, it may be necessary to amplify each signal first and then carry out the multiplexing prior to conversion (see Figure 4.9).

A cheaper and simpler way of equalising the signal voltages, so as to benefit from the maximum possible resolution on all inputs, is to attenuate the larger signals down to the value of the smallest. Thus, in the example just discussed, both the 15 mV and the 18 mV signals would need attenuating to 10 mV. A common amplifier would then serve all equally. Attenuation involves nothing more than two resistors per channel, as shown in Figure 4.10. It should not, however, be

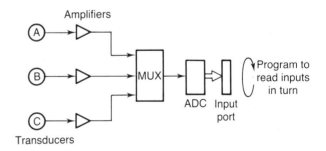

Figure 4.9 Use of post-amplification multiplexing

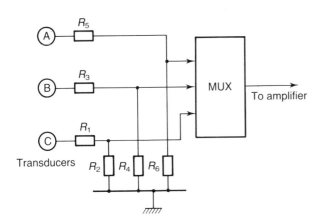

Figure 4.10 Equalising inputs of different levels by attenuation

$$\text{Gain for input A} = \frac{10}{10 \times 10^{-3}}$$
$$= 1000$$

Similarly, the gains for the other two inputs can be determined:

$$\text{Gain for input B} = \frac{10}{15 \times 10^{-3}}$$
$$= 667$$

$$\text{Gain for input C} = \frac{10}{18 \times 10^{-3}}$$
$$= 556$$

All gains have been rounded off to whole numbers.

To benefit from the saving in hardware, it is necessary to include in the program segment for each input the necessary instructions that will set the amplifier gain to the value required for that input.

used as a solution unless the variation in available signal levels between the channels is not too excessive. Too much attenuation of any given input will reduce the sensitivity of that input, perhaps unacceptably.

PROGRAMMABLE INSTRUMENTATION AMPLIFIER

In the last chapter, mention was made of an amplifier that is capable of being programmed by a digital input to give incremental gain control over an extremely wide range. This amplifier would be very useful in the situation just discussed. It would then only be necessary to determine how much gain each input required to match each signal to the full-scale input range of the converter. Having calculated the required gain, the program that generates the multiplexing codes could also program the amplifier for the correct gain value, as each input is selected.

To return to the situation of the three inputs, A, B and C just discussed, the required amplifier gains could be calculated as follows. For input A, providing 10 mV, the gain needed to raise this to the full-scale input of the converter is given by:

ANALOGUE SWITCHES

There are a number of useful CMOS analogue switches in the '4000' series of integrated circuits, that can be used for multiplexing applications. The multiplexing is carried out by sending sequential binary codes to the control pins of the ICs. Inhibit pins on the ICs allow the operation to be enabled or disabled by the logic levels on such pins. Some analogue switches have latches which 'freeze' the data and ignore subsequent changes until required to do so.

The 4051 and 4351 Analogue Switches

These are described as '1-pole 8-way' switches, since they will connect any one of eight analogue input signals to a common line, dependent upon the binary code on the three control pins. The inhibit pin (pin 6) of the 4051 must be low for switching to be allowed. On the 4351, pin 7 must be low and pin 8 high, to allow switching. Both devices are bi-directional, thus allowing them to be used for analogue demultiplexing as an alternative. The 4351 has the useful extra facility of being able to latch the input data as required. As long as the latch enable pin (pin 11) is low, the data cannot change, whether a channel is selected or not.

There are two variants of the basic switches, which differ mainly in terms of switching speeds. The 'straight' IC such as the CD4051BE is fairly slow, taking between about 120 ns and 360 ns to turn on or off, depending upon the value of the supply voltage. Its bandwidth is given as 20 MHz. The very much faster 74HC4051 device is able to switch on or off in the range 16–28 ns, again depending upon the supply voltage. The signal bandwidth for this device is 120 MHz. Similar comments apply to the 74HC4351.

The 4067 Analogue Switch

This is a 1-pole 16-way bi-directional switch, thus allowing the multiplexing of 16 individual analogue channels. Comments are much the same as for the 4051, the speed being slightly faster, with turn-on and turn-off times of the order of 75–240 ns. The maximum analogue signal that can be transmitted through the device is +15 V.

Multi-pole Switches

It is also possible to obtain IC packages containing several individual switches. Examples are the 4052BE (and 74HC4052), which is a 2-pole 4-way analogue switch, the 4053BE (and 74HC4053), a 3-pole 2-way switch and the 4016BE (and 74HC4016), which is 4-pole 1-way. The latter type is useful in sample-and-hold circuits.

A PRACTICAL EXAMPLE OF A MULTIPLEXED SYSTEM

Figure 4.11 shows the block diagram for a system with multiple inputs. The nature of the transducers is not identified, since it is not really relevant. What matters are the general principles, applicable to many situations. This system is based on the popular Z80 CPU and its associated Z80 PIO input/output chip. The ADC chosen is the ZN427E, whose input is driven from the output of an analogue amplifier. This latter receives a multiplexed input from a 4051 analogue switch. It is assumed that no other form of signal conditioning is required.

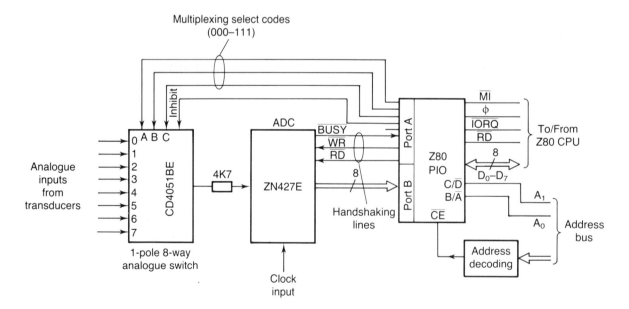

Figure 4.11   Practical example of a multiplexed system

Port A of the Z80 PIO is used to provide the handshake signals (three lines: $\overline{\text{Busy}}$, $\overline{\text{RD}}$ and $\overline{\text{WR}}$) for the ADC operation, as well as sending the appropriate codes to the 4051 (three lines plus the inhibit line) to select any given input. The multiplexing of the analogue inputs can be carried out on a cyclic basis, taking each input in turn. Equally easily it is possible to write software that will select any given input at any required instant. The data out of the ZN427E ADC is input at Port B of the PIO. Both ports of the PIO operate in Mode 3 (bit mode).

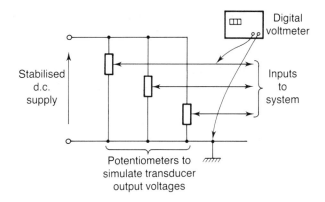

Figure 4.12 Method of providing test voltages for a system with multiple inputs

TESTING A SYSTEM WITH MULTIPLE INPUTS

Figure 4.12 shows a simple arrangement of potentiometers that can be used to simulate the voltage range of the system's transducers. This allows testing to proceed without having to establish the actual environment in which inputs would normally be received. By rotation of any of the input potentiometers, the full signal voltage range of the simulated transducer for that channel can be obtained. This variable can be measured accurately, in a series of steps, using a digital voltmeter, and the system's response observed. Again this need not actually involve connecting the system to any physical controllers. The effects can be judged from the electrical signals available at the outputs of the system. This, in turn, may mean nothing more than the manual reading of a series of voltage measurements, or may invoke the use of a pen recorder, plotter, printer, etc., to obtain a hard copy record of the system response.

Self-test Questions

4.1 Show how a 2-input AND gate and a toggle-type flip-flop can be used to convert Gray code into pure binary code.

If a 4-bit Gray-coded value 0 1 1 0 is to be converted into its pure binary equivalent, draw the waveforms at:

a) the output from the disk encoder,

b) the output of the AND gate,

c) the Q output of the flip-flop.

Hence, show that the conversion has been correctly effected.

4.2 Explain what is meant by a handshaking technique with regard to the transfer of data from a peripheral to a microcomputer.

4.3 Four transducers provide data for an environmentally controlled greenhouse. The outputs from three of the transducers are of similar amplitudes, while the third output is significantly smaller. Draw a block diagram and, using it, discuss the likely hardware requirements of the system prior to the actual conversion process.

4.4 Explain what is meant by multiplexing of analogue signals. What is its principal advantage?

4.5 Explain how a software program reading inputs into a computer can be said to be demultiplexing the signals from multiplexed inputs. What outputs to the multiplexer should the software generate?

FIVE

Analogue-to-digital and digital-to-analogue conversion

It has now been clearly established that the output available from the majority of transducers is of an analogue nature. Further, this signal may well need some conditioning for the reasons and in the manner discussed in Chapter Three. After such conditioning, one problem still remains. Since a digital computer can only handle binary data, the analogue signal must now be converted to digital form before the computer can accept and process it. This conversion is carried out by a particular type of interface circuit, known as an *Analogue-to-Digital Converter* (*ADC*).

Similarly, the digital output from the computer will almost certainly need to be converted to an analogue signal. This is true whether it is to drive an analogue process controller, or simply to log the value of the measured variable over a given time period, as in temperature/time plots, for example. The interface that performs this conversion is known as a *Digital-to-Analogue Converter* (*DAC*).

Naturally, there are the occasional exceptions, but in most control systems either or both of the above interfaces will be found. The general scheme of Figure 5.1 depicts a typical situation. In the system represented by this figure, an analogue transducer is being used to monitor some unspecified physical quantity; as a result, a

voltage is developed whose amplitude is proportional to the magnitude of that quantity. Possible situations are not difficult to bring to mind. Some possibilities include temperature, velocity (linear or angular), displacement (also linear or angular), pH factor of liquids, force, light intensity, and so on.

As discussed above, the output of this transducer, after suitable conditioning, will then be converted into an equivalent binary value, this

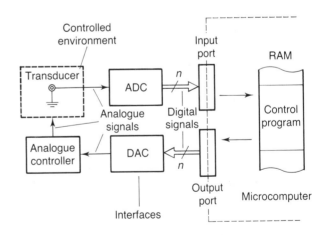

Figure 5.1 A practical situation requiring signal conversion, both analogue-to-digital (input) and digital-to-analogue (output)

taking place in the block marked ADC; the output from this block will be an *n*-bit parallel binary word. The minimum value of *n* is likely to be eight, making it compatible with the standard input/output ports and data bus of 8-bit micro-computers.

The binary output from the ADC will enter the computer at another specialised interface known generally as a *port*. Logically, for this part of the operation, this port is termed an *input port*. The program, which is run by the microcomputer, will periodically examine the data input at this port and 'process' it. Where the computer is being employed in a control loop, this program will probably now compare this received data with some reference value and, from the result of the comparison, generate an appropriate binary control signal. This control signal will then be output through another port, in this case, an *output port*.

The controller, assuming it to be an analogue device, will not be able to respond directly to this binary signal. Therefore, the signal will have to undergo a conversion into an equivalent analogue form in the block marked DAC.

ANALOGUE-TO-DIGITAL CONVERSION

Because the digital-to-analogue conversion process is the easier of the two, it is tempting to describe the techniques of this process first. It also happens that there is less variety in the circuits used. However, to preserve a continuous approach to what might be termed the 'signal path', the order will be reversed. Thus, having discussed, in earlier chapters, the generation and subsequent conditioning of the transduced voltage or current, it seems totally logical to look next at the principles involved in the conversion of that signal into the digital form that the computer requires. Actual circuits, of which there is a great variety, can be described later once the basic ideas have been assimilated.

Sampling the Input

It is easy to think of the analogue output from the transducer as if it were constant, an assumption that almost certainly will not be true. There are physical quantities that may, more often than not, vary extremely slowly, temperature being an example. Others, such as displacement, velocity and acceleration, may vary extremely rapidly. If, at some instant in time, the analogue input is converted into its digital equivalent, all that has actually been done is to express the signal's digital value *at that instant only*; it may well be quite different a short time later. To represent the analogue quantity in a meaningful manner, it must be *sampled* (that is, captured and measured) repeatedly, and at a frequency that bears some relationship to its rate of variation.

Figure 5.2 should help to make this clear, showing an analogue signal that is being sampled at successive instants of time so as to keep track of the varying nature of the signal. Note that several conversions are made for every cycle of the input waveform; a sine wave input is shown in this figure, but the principle is correct whatever the nature of

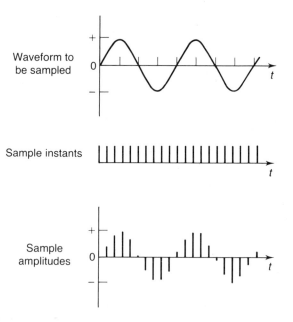

Figure 5.2 The process of sampling a sine wave

the varying analogue input voltage. This process of converting samples of the input at successive times is, naturally, called sampling. The more samples that are taken during the period of the input, the more accurately does the digital data represent the nature of the analogue signal. Obviously there is a limit to the number of times a signal can be sampled in any given time period. Also, the higher the frequency of the analogue input, the more difficult does it become to sample it often enough.

The *Shannon sampling theorem* states that, 'the rate at which a signal is sampled should be at least twice that of the highest frequency component in the sampled signal if the analogue input is to be effectively represented'.

Conversion Time

The statement made earlier, regarding sampling the analogue input 'at some instant of time', is actually a simplification of the true situation. The conversion process, turning the analogue signal into an *n*-bit binary value, is often far from instantaneous and takes an amount of time, as will be seen later, that depends upon the type of converter. Some are extremely slow to convert; others are very fast indeed. If a signal varies rapidly, it makes sense to take samples often and quickly. For quantities that vary only slowly, the length of the conversion process is not so important a criterion. In either case, there is the likelihood that the signal amplitude will vary to a greater or lesser degree during the time of the conversion cycle.

Sample-and-hold Circuits

The solution to the problem stated in the previous paragraph is to freeze the sample at the start of conversion, this process taking negligible time compared with the conversion time itself. The converter then performs its function of digitising this sample, after which the latter is released and a new sample taken. The reason for calling the circuit that performs this vital task a *sample-and-hold* circuit should therefore be obvious.

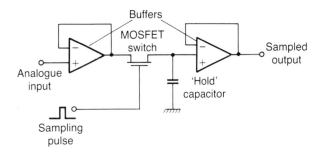

Figure 5.3 A sample-and-hold circuit

Figure 5.3 shows a sample-and-hold circuit in which a FET switch is used to connect the buffered analogue input voltage to the 'hold' capacitor during the brief duration of the sampling pulse. The hold capacitor is also buffered to reduce the possibility of leakage during the conversion period. At some instant of time, the FET switch is closed (FET conducting) by a short duration pulse. The hold capacitor will now charge up to the instantaneous value of the analogue voltage. The FET switch then opens (FET non-conducting). The voltage held in the capacitor is now the input to the converter, which commences its conversion cycle. When the cycle is complete and the data has been accepted by the computer, the FET switch will be closed by a further pulse and the hold capacitor will charge (or discharge) to a new value of analogue voltage. This in turn, will be converted, the process repeating indefinitely.

FULL-SCALE RANGE, QUANTISATION AND QUANTISATION INTERVALS

It is fundamental to a digital signal that there are discrete intervals between successive values. The analogue signal, by comparison, varies continuously. As a result, the converter output will invariably be a close approximation to the analogue input, rather than an exact equivalent. In Figure 5.4, the transfer characteristic of a 4-bit ADC shows that there are only $2^4 = 16$ discrete

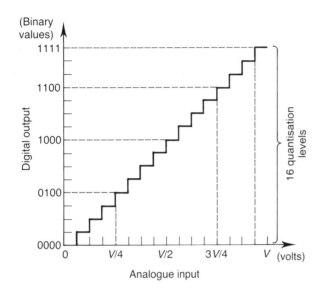

Figure 5.4 The transfer characteristic of a 4-bit ADC, showing the 16 discrete levels possible

binary values available to represent all the possible analogue values (an infinite number!) between the minimum and maximum signal limits. The closeness of the approximation can be improved by increasing the number of bits contained in the binary result. For example, if the converter has eight bits instead of four, there will then be $2^8 = 256$ possible values. Taking a further example, a 12-bit converter will have $2^{12} = 4096$ different values.

In Figure 5.4 each of the dotted lines corresponds to a digital value that is the exact equivalent of some particular analogue value on the horizontal axis. The process of approximating to an analogue voltage in this way is called *quantisation* and the discrete levels are called *quantisation levels*.

A given converter will accept a particular range of analogue input voltage. Logically, the maximum permissible analogue input will generate the largest possible binary output. Thus, there is a direct scale relationship between analogue input and binary output. Either of these quantities could be said to express the Full-Scale Range (FSR) of the converter.

To consider this matter further, assume that the range of the analogue input lies between

0 V and 4 V and that this occupies the FSR. Taking three converters in turn, of equal FSR but different bit value:

> The 4-bit converter has 16 values, hence 15 quantisation intervals between one value and the next. Thus, the range 0–4 V will be converted in analogue steps each having a value of 4/15 = 0.27 V. These are quite large steps, so the resulting error can be significant.
>
> The 8-bit converter, having 256 values, has 255 such intervals, each of which is equivalent to 4/255 = 0.02 V. A much better situation.
>
> The 12-bit converter is obviously going to be significantly better than either of the others. In real terms, its 4095 levels will each have a value of 0.000 97 V, or 0.97 mV.

The ability of a converter to generate a binary value approximating as closely as possible to the analogue input is expressed by its *resolution*. Obviously, there is a relationship between resolution and the number of bits in the converted value. This is another way of saying that resolution is related to the number of quantisation levels.

Resolution can be expressed in several ways, as follows. Taking as an example, a 10-bit converter.

(a) It may be said to have 10-bit resolution.
(b) It may be said to have a resolution of 1 part in 2^{10} i.e. 1 in 1024.
(c) It may be expressed as an absolute voltage, e.g. for a full-scale voltage of 5 V, the resolution would be approximately 5/1024 V, which equals 4.88 mV.
(d) It may be expressed as a percentage. In case (c), the voltage 4.88 mV related to the full-scale value of 5 V can be expressed as

$$\left(\frac{4.88 \times 10^{-3}}{5}\right) \times (100\%) = 0.0976\%$$

Resolution and Accuracy

It is interesting to consider what happens if an analogue signal is first put through a process that converts it into a series of digital samples and is then put through the reverse process that converts these samples back into an analogue

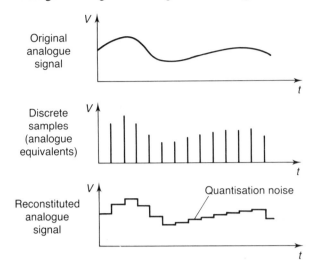

Figure 5.5 The result of converting and then re-converting an analogue signal

signal. Ideally one would end up with an exact replica of the original analogue signal. Figure 5.5 shows that this will certainly not be true, especially if the converter uses only a small number of bits.

In this figure a series of digital samples of a waveform are taken which, when converted back, produce a corresponding series of steps; this is the reconstituted analogue waveform. A quite marked difference is evident between the original and reconstituted waveforms. There is an amplitude fluctuation now that was not present in the original signal; this higher frequency variation is given the name *quantisation noise*. This noise can be reduced in value if the signal is passed through a low-pass filter. The greater the difference between the fundamental signal frequency and the quantisation noise frequency, the better will be the filtering. This is just another way of saying that the higher the sampling frequency, the better!

It is obvious from the above that the *accuracy* with which a conversion is effected is related to the resolution of the converter. However, resolution and accuracy, while related, are not the same thing.

Accuracy specifies how closely the actual value of some quantity approaches the correct value.

For example, if a converter (DAC), for a given binary input produces an output of 3.5 V, when the output ought to be 3.6 V, quite clearly there is an error. The absolute magnitude of this error is – 0.1 V. Similarly, one can express the accuracy in terms of the difference between the obtained binary value (in the case of an ADC) and the true binary value. It is quite possible to have a converter with excellent resolution yet poor accuracy, and vice versa.

THE CONVERTER/COMPUTER LINKUP

The object of an ADC is to provide the computer with digital data at its input port. As has already been seen, conversion may be quite a slow process, certainly when compared with the rate at which the computer can handle data. This makes it necessary to synchronise the two rates in some way. This may be done by linking the ADC to two available input/output lines of the computer, these two lines having control functions which could be known as Start Convert and Status. These lines allow the converter and computer to perform a hand-shaking procedure as follows. Figure 5.6 shows a converter coupled to a computer so as to implement this procedure.

The computer will initiate the conversion process by sending a pulse to the ADC, on the Start Convert line; this is readily generated by software or by a hardware timer. At this time, when the conversion starts, the Status line will be taken to a predetermined logic level (usually logic 1) to signify that the ADC is now Busy. At the end of the conversion process, the logic level of the Status line will invert to indicate that it has now returned to the Ready state.

The question could be asked, 'what is the computer doing while the conversion is being carried out?' There are two possibilities; either the computer is doing something else – usually running the 'main program' – or it is doing nothing, merely waiting in a loop for the Ready signal to appear on the Status line.

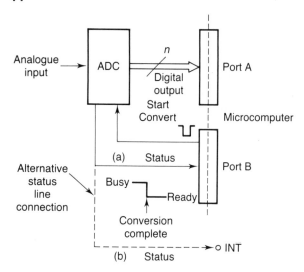

Figure 5.6 The converter/computer link-up: (a) software-controlled conversion, (b) an interrupt-driven converter

In the former case, the computer will need to be 'interrupted' from the program that it is running in order to carry out the alternative task of collecting the data now available at the input port. In such a situation, the Status line would be connected to the INT interrupt input so that, when the Status line goes low, an interrupt service routine is called to input the new data.

DIGITAL-TO-ANALOGUE CONVERSION

The process of converting the digital output from the computer into its analogue equivalent is much simpler and faster than the reverse process. There are, in theory at least, two possible circuits to do this, both of which will be described shortly. In practice, only one of these has much real value, for reasons that will be explained. Certain limitations arise, as one might expect, and it will be worth looking at these before going further with the actual methods.

Resolution has a similar meaning in this process. Conversion from an *n*-bit digital signal to an analogue one does not involve any rounding

up or down of the values; every binary value yields an exact analogue equivalent. Nonetheless, the better the resolution, in terms of the number of bits in the original binary value, the greater will be the possible number of analogue increments, and the finer the control that the computer can exercise.

Although the expression 'exact ... equivalent' was used above, this does not imply that inaccuracies cannot occur. In fact, they will and do, but careful design will minimise them.

Speed of conversion is extremely fast, because of the basic principles involved. This point will be appreciated more fully later, when some actual circuits are discussed. It is limited by the *settling time*, which is the time taken for the converted value to settle within $\pm\frac{1}{2}$LSB, between one digital quantity and the next. The worst case occurs when all bits in the binary signal have to change between successive values of the signal. This is illustrated by the consecutive binary numbers 0 1 1 1 1 1 1 1 and 1 0 0 0 0 0 0 0; all eight bits change between the two numbers. A typical value for settling time is around 0.3–1.0 μs.

It is possible for a particular type of error, known as *gain error* to occur. This results from a shift in the input/output relation owing to changes in the reference voltage with which the converter must be supplied. A well-stabilised supply should eliminate this cause of error.

Principles of Digital-to-analogue Conversion

The process of converting a digital signal into an analogue one is relatively simple, both in principle and in hardware design. The two possible methods mentioned previously are both shown in Figure 5.7.

The method of Figure 5.7(a) relies upon using resistors whose values are 'weighted' according to the columns of the binary value to be converted. Actually, the resistor values are in inverse ratio to the weightings of the binary columns, so as to produce currents flowing into the junction that are in direct proportion to the column weightings. So, since a 4-bit binary number is weighted 8421,

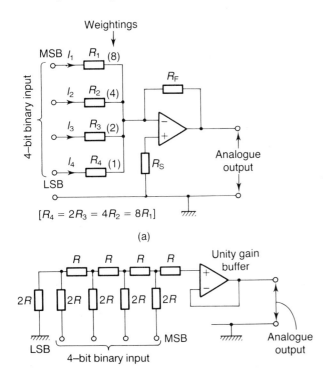

Figure 5.7 Two 4-bit DACs compared: (a) the 'weighted resistor' type and (b) the $R, 2R$ ladder network

analysis can it be shown that this circuit actually works (or by practical experiment of course!). The role of the opamp in this case is to act as a unity gain buffer between the converter output and the analogue device following.

It is important that the binary logic levels to the converter, of either type, should be consistent. The actual source of the digital data must not be used directly as the input since, in any practical system, tolerances are allowed on logic 0 and logic 1 levels that would cause significant errors if they were used as converter inputs. By using the binary input simply to energise analogue switches, consistent values of voltage will always be applied to the resistor network. The scaling of the converter will then be consistent across its full input range, since all logic 0 levels will be truly zero, and all logic 1 levels will equal the reference voltage applied to the converter. A 4-bit $R, 2R$ converter with analogue switches is shown in Figure 5.8.

the current I_1 in resistor R_1 is twice the current in R_2, four times that in R_3 and eight times that in R_4, for the cases when the input is a logic 1. The output voltage V_o is proportional to the binary number input, thus achieving the required conversion. The opamp is used as a 'summing' amplifier in this example. Although it may not be an obvious drawback, this circuit has the disadvantage of requiring a wide range of different resistor values, especially with 8-bit and higher order converters. This would not matter quite so much if the design were intended to be built discretely, but present practice is to use film or semiconductor resistor networks.

The $R, 2R$ ladder network DAC of Figure 5.7(b) overcomes this drawback. As its name implies it uses only two different resistor values, with a simple 2 : 1 relation between them, no matter how many bits are converted. Only by network

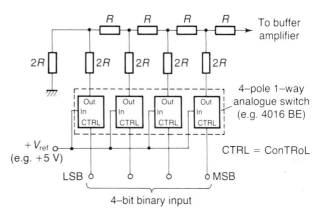

Figure 5.8 A practical $R, 2R$ converter must use analogue switches

ANALOGUE-TO-DIGITAL CONVERTERS

There is an interesting variety of circuits for the process of analogue-to-digital conversion. A few of these will show how varied the principles of conversion are.

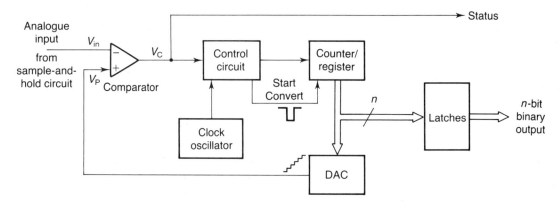

Figure 5.9   The continuous-balance ADC

The Continuous-balance ADC

The schematic circuit for this type is shown in Figure 5.9. This circuit contains a DAC, normally of the $R, 2R$ type, within the loop. The function of the control circuit is to gate clock pulses to the input of the counter/register section. The latter is just a binary counter with the output buffered by a register which may have parallel or serial output (parallel shown in this case). The state of the control circuit, that is, whether it enables or disables the counter input pulses, is determined by the output voltage V_C from the comparator. There are two analogue inputs to the comparator, (a) the voltage V_{in} to be converted and (b) the output from the DAC V_P, this being the analogue equivalent of whatever binary value the counter is holding.

Assume that, initially, the counter/register has been cleared by the Start Convert pulse; the output from the DAC is obviously zero ($V_P = 0$). Assume that a voltage V_{in} is present that is to be converted. Therefore, $V_{in} > V_P$ and V_C 'enables' the counter which begins to count up. The output from the DAC rises in a series of small steps as the counter value increases, until there comes a point where $V_P = V_{in}$ and then just exceeds it. The output of the comparator V_C switches to the opposite polarity and 'disables' the counter, which then stops. The comparator output would also provide the Status level output to the

computer. The binary value held by the counter/register is the equivalent of the analogue input. The process would repeat on receipt of a new Start Convert pulse.

This is one of the slower types of converter. The length of the conversion process depends upon the size of the analogue input. For an analogue input voltage equal to the full-scale input, the counter has to count up to its limit. An N-bit counter needs $(2^N - 1)$ clock cycles to complete the conversion. An 8-bit counter using a 1 MHz clock would take $2^8 - 1 = 255\,\mu s$ to convert the largest input voltage.

The Dual-slope ADC

This type of converter, shown in Figure 5.10, is used frequently in digital voltmeters, but is also sometimes used in computer input circuits. In contrast with the converter just described, it does not make use of a DAC.

To start the conversion process the switch S (an electronic one) is set to select the analogue input voltage V_{in}; at this instant, referred to on the graph as t_0, the output V_o from the ramp generator is 0 V, as a result of which the comparator output is such as to enable the counter via the control circuit; the latter, also starting from zero, commences an up-counting sequence. While this is happening, the output of the ramp generator is a voltage of negative slope, this slope being equal

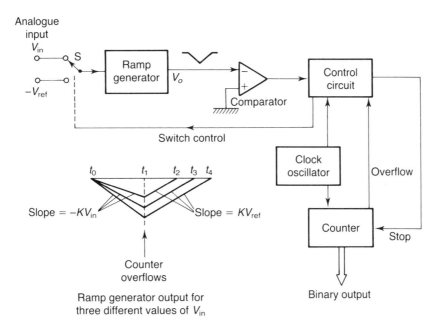

Ramp generator output for
three different values of V_{in}

Figure 5.10   The dual-slope ADC

to $-KV_{in}$. Eventually, the counter will reach its maximum value and, with one more clock pulse, will overflow. This latter event is detected by the control circuit which immediately switches S over to select the $-V_{ref}$ input.

Considering this instant in time when the counter has just overflowed, termed t_1, the ramp voltage has a value that is directly proportional to V_{in} and the contents of the counter are also zero at this moment. From this point in time two events commence simultaneously. The counter begins to count up again and the output of the ramp generator rises in a positive direction, this time with a slope KV_{ref}. When the ramp generator output reaches 0 V the output of the comparator will invert and cause the control unit to disable the counter. The binary value held by the counter is directly proportional to the time taken for the ramp to return to zero. Since the rate at which it does so is always constant it follows that the time taken to return to zero depends upon the value of the negative voltage from which it started. As already stated, the latter in turn depends upon the value of V_{in}, the analogue input – hence the relation between the analogue and the digital outputs.

This type of converter suffers from the same speed limitations as the continuous-balance type for the same reasons.

THE SUCCESSIVE APPROXIMATION REGISTER ADC

The Successive Approximation Register (SAR) type of converter represents an ingenious way of obtaining high speed of operation without great complexity. It is an example of another type that makes use of a DAC. The schematic diagram is shown in Figure 5.11.

The principle is quite simple. The converter starts by making a 'guess' at the value of the binary number required and then follows this initial value with a series of successive approximations, by a totally logical procedure, until it gets it right. A voltage comparator is used to signal when this state has been achieved. An example will make this quite clear.

Suppose that the actual binary value that an 8-bit converter should produce is 1 0 0 1 1 0 1 1 (which of course we do not know at the moment!).

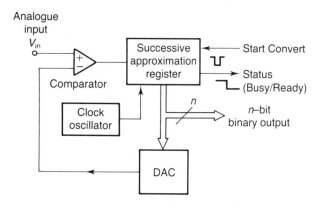

Figure 5.11 A successive approximation register ADC

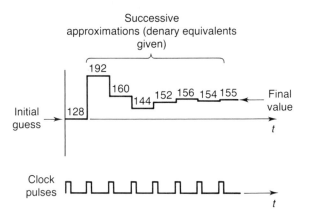

Figure 5.12 Showing how the output of a successive approximation converter converges to the final value

The converter always starts by making the same initial guess, this being the mid-range value of the largest possible binary number that the converter is capable of producing; for an 8-bit converter this would be 1 1 1 1 1 1 1 1, leading to a mid-range value of 1 0 0 0 0 0 0 0. In this specific case, the comparator would tell the successive approximation logic that this guess is too low. The procedure then is that the next MSB is set, giving 1 1 0 0 0 0 0 0. This is clearly too large now, as the comparator will signify, so the second MSB is taken out again and the next MSB set. The procedure continues along these lines, the binary value oscillating above and below the required value (see Figure 5.12), but gradually converging towards it until the correct value is obtained. The sequence will look like this:

Clock pulse	SAR contents	Comparator result
1	1 0 0 0 0 0 0 0	Too Low
2	1 1 0 0 0 0 0 0	Too High
3	1 0 1 0 0 0 0 0	Too High
4	1 0 0 1 0 0 0 0	Too Low
5	1 0 0 1 1 0 0 0	Too Low
6	1 0 0 1 1 1 0 0	Too High
7	1 0 0 1 1 0 1 0	Too Low
8	1 0 0 1 1 0 1 1	Correct

One thing that should be evident immediately is that it only took eight clock pulses to carry out the complete conversion. Some conversions will, of course, take less but none will ever exceed n, the number of bits being converted.

To emphasise the matter of speed once more, consider 12-bit converters of the continuous-balance and SAR types, both using a 1 MHz clock. At this clock frequency, the length of one cycle is $1/10^6$ s or one microsecond.

For the continuous-balance type of ADC, the maximum conversion time is obtained from:

$$\text{Maximum conversion time} = \frac{\text{Number of clock pulses to reach maximum count}}{\times} \times \text{Time of one clock cycle}$$

The number of clock pulses to reach maximum count = $2^n - 1$, where n is the number of bits of the converter. In this case, n is 12, so that the maximum conversion time works out at $(2^{12} - 1)$ μs, which is 4095 μs.

By comparison the same conversion carried out by the SAR type would take just n μs = 12 μs! This is for the reason already stated, that the maximum number of clock cycles for a conversion equals the number of bits converted.

The hardware for the successive approximation type of converter can be reduced by using software to run the successive approximation process.

Flash Converters

Converters of this type are extremely fast. The schematic for a flash converter is shown in Figure 5.13, together with its truth table.

The resistive potential divider establishes threshold voltages on the non-inverting inputs of the comparators. The voltage at the top of the

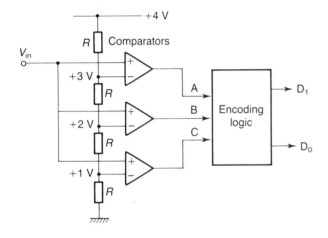

V_{in} (V)	Comparator outputs			Binary output	
	C	B	A	D_1	D_0
0–1	0	0	0	0	0
1–2	1	0	0	0	1
2–3	1	1	0	1	0
3–4	1	1	1	1	1

Figure 5.13   The flash converter type of ADC, a very fast circuit

divider is equal to the full-scale analogue voltage of the converter. The inverting inputs to the comparators are all commoned and connected to the source of analogue voltage. The output from any comparator will go high if the voltage on its

non-inverting input exceeds the reference voltage on its inverting input. Thus, as the analogue input is increased from zero towards its maximum possible value, the outputs of the comparators go high in succession. This leads to a different code output for each discrete level of input. This code must then go through a conversion process to produce a true binary output that corresponds to the analogue input. This is carried out in the *encoding logic* block.

The speed of response of this type of converter is limited only by the switching times of the comparators and encoding logic. The response being virtually instantaneous, the device is therefore termed a *flash converter*. To obtain sufficient resolution a very large number of comparators is required – one for each quantisation level – a problem which only large-scale integration can solve economically.

COMMERCIALLY AVAILABLE CONVERTER ICs

There are many ADCs and DACs in inexpensive IC form. The following is a sample of various types, with brief details of their features and an indication of their performance.

ADC0804   This is an 8-bit CMOS ADC which has a latched output that can drive a microprocessor data bus directly. The IC can be addressed as a memory location or input/output port, making it easy to integrate into the system, no special interfacing being required. The normal analogue voltage input range is 0–5 V but it is possible to scale the input to any smaller range, still retaining the full 8-bit resolution. This is achieved by programming pin 9 with a reference voltage equal to half the input voltage range.

For example, if the analogue voltage range were only 3 V, then a voltage equal to 1.5 V should be established at pin 9, by means of a potential divider.

It is similarly possible to 'offset the zero' so as to have an analogue voltage with a non-zero

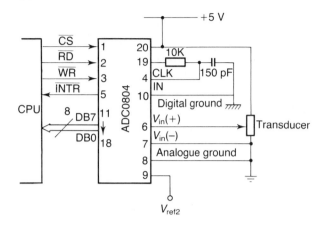

Figure 5.14 System connections for the ADC0804 converter

origin. For example, if the input is scaled to have a range of 3 V, this need not run from 0–3 V, but could occupy the voltage span from 0.75–3.75 V if required.

The maximum conversion rate is specified at 8770 conversions/second. The supply current is only 1.3 mA. Accuracy is ± 1 LSB. Figure 5.14 shows the system connection details for this IC.

ADC0820 This is a high-speed ADC that uses the *half-flash* technique where 32 comparators handle the most and least significant bits sequentially in two 4-bit ADCs. No external sample-and-hold circuitry is needed, since the input to the IC is tracked and held by input sampling circuitry,

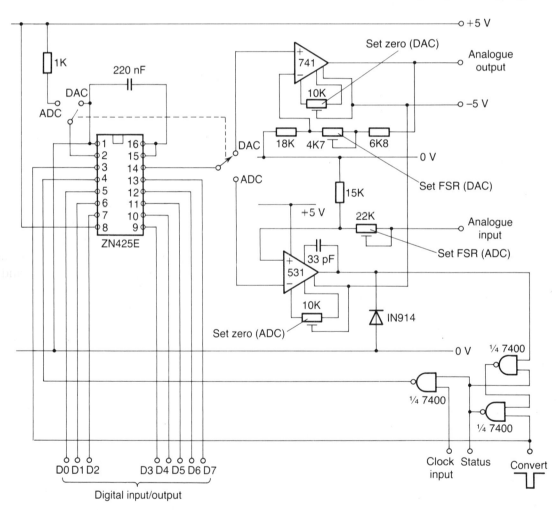

Figure 5.15 An application circuit for the ZN425E converter

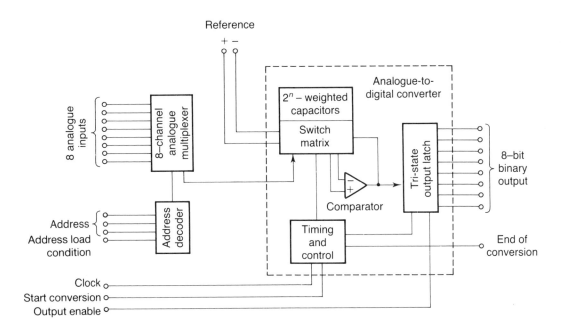

Figure 5.16 Block diagram of the Si520 'system on a chip' converter

provided that the input rate of change does not exceed 100 mV/μs. The outputs are tri-state and the IC appears to the microprocessor as either a memory location or an input/output port.

The conversion time is only 1.5 μs, making it a very fast device indeed. The supply voltage is + 5 V, the supply current, 7.5 mA and the analogue input voltage range is 0–5 V.

ZN425E This useful IC has on board an 8-bit DAC, a counter and a 2.5 V precision voltage reference. It can therefore perform either the role of DAC as it stands or, by adding an external comparator and clock inhibit gating, it can be used as a counter-ramp type ADC. For those who wish to have a device that can be switched into either mode at will, this IC is ideal. An application circuit is given in Figure 5.15 which shows how the dual role may be achieved.

ZN427E This 8-bit ADC is an example of a successive approximation converter. It contains a voltage-switching DAC, a fast comparator, successive approximation logic and a 2.56 V

precision voltage source. The conversion time using a 1 MHz clock is 10 μs. The supply voltage is in the range 4.5–5.5 V, with a supply current requirement of 25 mA. The accuracy is ±0.5 LSB.

ZN428E This device is complementary to the ZN427E. The digital input is latched, so that updating from a microcomputer data bus can be handled. The settling time is 800 ns and the linearity error ±0.5 LSB. The supply voltage requirement is 4.5–5.5 V at 20 mA.

Si520 This device is more of a 'system on a chip' than the others! It comprises an 8-channel, 8-bit CMOS data acquisition system with the following on board: an 8-channel multiplexer; a sample-and-hold function; an 8-bit ADC and microprocessor compatible logic.

The channels are selected by a 3-bit binary code. Thus, cycling through the binary sequence 0 0 0 – 1 1 1, a simple counting process, will select all channels in sequence at the counting rate. Each input is sampled and held stable during the conversion process. It is possible to select the required analogue input voltage range by means of a reference voltage. Both the multiplexer address inputs and the digital output are latched and are tri-state.

The supply voltage is nominally 5 V, but may lie in the range 3–5.5 V at a current of 10 μA. The conversion time, with a 100 kHz clock, is 70 μs. The total unadjusted error is ±0.25 LSB. Figure 5.16 shows a block diagram of the device.

Self-test Questions

5.1 By discussion, justify the need for analogue-to-digital conversion and digital-to-analogue conversion in a microprocessor control system.

5.2 What is meant by sampling an analogue signal? Why is it necessary? If an analogue signal has a frequency of 400 Hz what, according to the Shannon sampling theorem, is the *minimum* rate at which it should be sampled?

5.3 Discuss the role of a sample-and-hold circuit in the conversion process from an analogue to a digital signal. Draw a diagram for a sample-and-hold circuit and explain how it works.

5.4 An analogue signal, input to an ADC, has a range from 0 to +5 V. If the binary number output from the converter has 12 bits, what is the smallest change in the analogue signal that can be resolved? How many quantisation intervals has this converter?

5.5 If the full-scale range of a 12-bit converter is 8 V, what is its resolution expressed as (a) a voltage (b) a percentage?

5.6 What is the main advantage of the R, $2R$ type of converter over the weighted-resistor type of converter?

5.7 Explain why the binary inputs to a DAC should always be applied via analogue switches and not directly to the converter inputs.

5.8 Discuss the basic principles of the continuous-balance and successive-approximation types of converter. Assuming that a converter of each type has a resolution of eight bits and uses a 100 kHz clock frequency, how do their maximum conversion times compare?

SIX

Data transfers

SERIAL VERSUS PARALLEL

When digital data is transmitted from one device to another, there are two ways in which it can be done. The bits may all be sent at once, each bit having its own line; this is known as *parallel transmission*. Alternatively, the bits may be sent one at a time, in sequence, in what may be called a *bit stream*. This is known, logically, as *serial transmission*. Obviously with this latter method only a single line (plus a return) will be needed.

There are two arguments in favour of sending data serially. The most obvious one is that only the two conductors just mentioned, one forward and one return, are required, no matter how many data bits there are in the words being transmitted. This has an obvious cost advantage in terms of cabling. The second reason for making use of serial transmission is the ready availability of custom interfaces conforming to accepted standards and thus reducing the risks of physical incompatibilities between the computer and peripherals.

Within a computer the data is transmitted on a set of parallel conductors, known collectively as the *data bus*. Because all bits of a data word are sent simultaneously, the speed of transmission is very much higher than for the serial case. For parallel transmission of data, in general, the cost is, of course, the need for one conductor per bit of the parallel data word. This increases the complexity of the circuit board within the computer and demands a higher cost in terms of cabling external to the computer.

THE NATURE OF SERIAL DATA

As already stated, in the case of serial transmission the data bits are sent one at a time, in the form of a bit stream or *data stream*. Each bit in a data word is allocated its own 'slot in time'. Since the transmission of data in serial form is continuous, but with each data word having a finite length (e.g. eight bits), it is necessary to 'frame' each word with start and stop bits; this complete set of bits may be referred to as a *data packet*. Usually a serial line will idle in the logic 1 state until a start bit signals to the receiving equipment that a data packet is imminent. A typical serial data packet is shown in Figure 6.1.

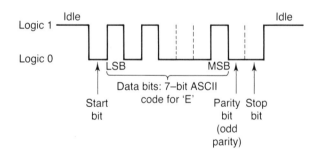

Figure 6.1 A typical serial data packet, showing the allocations of the bits

It comprises the start bit (at logic 0), followed by eight data bits, ending with the stop bit, also a logic 0 level, before returning to the logic 1 idling state. The LSB is usually sent first. The number of stop bits may variously be 1, 1½ or 2 bits.

BAUD RATES

Many serial links are said to be asynchronous, which means that a common clock signal is not sent along with the data. This implies that the frequencies of the data streams must be identical at both the sending and receiving ends. There are a number of standard frequencies which are actually termed *baud rates*, these being generally understood to mean the number of bits of data transmitted per second. This is not always strictly true but is close enough for most purposes. The range of baud rates extends from 50 to 19 200. The lower speeds were originally used for slow electromechanical devices, such as teletypes (though it is doubtful if much use is made of these nowadays). The highest speeds are for serial communication with a VDU or with another computer system.

PARITY

The continuous transmission of data in the way described above leads to the ever-present possibility of some of the data bits being corrupted, especially if the connecting cables pass through an electrically noisy environment. Such corruption of data would mean the inversion of one or more bits; that is, a logic 0 becomes a logic 1 or vice versa. Without some means of detecting such errors the transmitted data would be accepted at the receiving end without question. The simplest technique involves sending an extra bit, known as the *parity bit*, with the data word.

There are two strategies that can be followed in determining the value of a parity bit. They are known as *even parity* and *odd parity*.

In the case of even parity, the number of 1s in the word is counted; if this number is even, the parity bit takes the value 0 – so that the total number of 1s in the data plus parity bit is even. If, however, the number of 1s in the data word is odd, the parity bit takes the value 1 – again ensuring that there is an even number of 1s in the data packet.

Odd parity follows logically from this, the value of the parity bit being chosen so that there is always an odd number of 1s in the data packet.

The following examples should make this clear:

Data	Parity bit	
	Even	Odd
0 1 0 1 0 1 0 1	0	1
0 1 1 0 1 1 1 0	1	0
0 0 0 1 0 0 1 1	1	0
1 1 1 1 1 1 1 1	0	1

To conclude the argument, in case there are some lingering doubts, consider the first of the above examples, which is the data word 0 1 0 1 0 1 0 1; this quite clearly contains an even number of 1s, namely four. If this data word is to be sent with even parity then the parity bit must be 0 since the number of 1s in the word is already even. However, if the data word is to be sent with odd parity, then the parity bit must be a 1 in order that the total number of 1s transmitted is odd (five).

The natural question that follows from the above is, 'how is the parity bit used to detect an error?' It must be said at the beginning that this particular method of error checking using a single parity bit is not very sophisticated and will only detect errors where an odd number of bits becomes corrupted. For example, suppose the data word 1 0 0 1 1 0 1 0 is sent as even parity; the parity bit will be 0. Hence, the data word plus parity bit will look like this:

$$1 0 0 1 1 0 1 0 \text{ (data)} + 0 \text{ (parity)}$$

This quite clearly contains an even number of 1s as expected by the receiver and the word will be accepted without question – which is just as well, since it happens to be correct.

Suppose that one bit of the data word becomes corrupted; for example the second MSB of the data word changes from 0 to 1. The data word plus parity bit now looks like this:

$$1 1 0 1 1 0 1 0 \text{ (data)} + 0 \text{ (parity)}$$

If the 1s are now counted at the receiver, the number will be found to be odd. Since the receiver is expecting an even number it will know that an error has occurred and will probably ask for that last data word to be re-transmitted.

The problem arises, as already mentioned, when an even number of errors occurs. For example, if both the second MSB and the next bit below both corrupt to 1s, then the received data will be:

$$1\ 1\ 1\ 1\ 1\ 0\ 1\ 0\ \text{(data)}\ +\ 0\ \text{(parity)}$$

The data is incorrect but will be accepted since the number of 1s is even (six), thus conforming to even parity.

Not all serial links employ the parity bit for checking. They either leave it permanently set (equals 1) or clear (equals 0) or omit it completely.

DATA TRANSFER MODES: SIMPLEX, FULL-DUPLEX AND HALF-DUPLEX

When data is transmitted serially, the method used will conform to one of the schemes described below. These refer to the nature of the link between transmitting and receiving devices.

- A *simplex* data link allows the transmission of data in one direction only.
- In a *full-duplex* data link, simultaneous transmission of data in both directions is possible.
- In a *half-duplex* data link, transmission of data can take place in either direction but only on an alternate basis. That is, while one device is transmitting, the other is listening, or vice versa.

These modes of operation are illustrated in Figure 6.2.

PARALLEL/SERIAL CONVERSION

When a serial data link is used, for example between two computers, the parallel data format used within each computer has to be converted into a serial format in order to use the single line

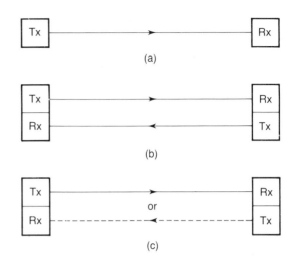

Figure 6.2 Illustrating (a) simplex (b) full-duplex and (c) half-duplex modes of serial data transmission

data path between the devices. There are a number of dedicated LSI chips available for this function, some of which will be discussed briefly. Among those available are the following:

UART Universal Asynchronous Receiver/Transmitter

ACIA Asynchronous Communications Interface Adaptor

USART Universal Synchronous/Asynchronous Receiver/Transmitter

SIO Serial Input/Output device

The required functions of the above ICs can be summed up as follows, before looking at each one in more detail:

(a) Use a shift register to perform the serial/parallel or parallel/serial conversion.
(b) Select the required baud rate, number of data bits and stop bits.
(c) Establish the procedure to be adopted in the event of an error being detected.
(d) Signal the state of the input or output buffer, either full or empty.

The 6402 UART

This is an industry standard UART, the block diagram of both the transmit and receive circuitry

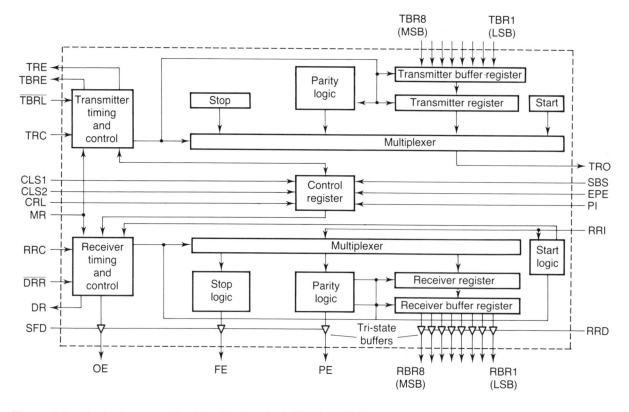

Figure 6.3   Block diagram of the industry standard 6402 UART IC

being shown in Figure 6.3. To explain in full how the device is used would occupy an unreasonable amount of space, but an outline of its operation will be given here. This device can be used in a wide range of applications including modems, printers, various other peripherals and remote data acquisition systems. The CMOS/LSI technology used permits clock frequencies up to 4 MHz with a power consumption of 10 mW or less.

Some aspects of the UART operation are software controlled and some are determined by hardwiring certain of the pin connections. In particular the pins known as CLS2, CLS1, PI, EPE and SBS will be hardwired to a given pattern (from 32 possible patterns) of logic 0s and logic 1s to select the required parameters for: number of data bits (5, 6, 7 or 8), parity even, odd or disabled; the number of stop bits (1, 1½ or 2). These pins are defined as follows:

(a) CLS2 and CLS1 (Character Length Selected) allow four binary combinations, corresponding to the four permitted word lengths of 5, 6, 7 or 8 bits specified above.
(b) PI (Parity Inhibited): this condition is obtained when this pin is high (logic 1).
(c) EPE (Even Parity Enabled): a high level on this pin produces even parity (on transmission) and checks it (on reception).
(d) SBS has two functions when at logic 1, depending upon the selected word length: for a 5-bit word it produces 1½ stop bits and 2 stop bits for other word lengths; however, if SBS is at logic 0 it produces 1 stop bit.

There is a relationship between the clock frequency and the baud rate. The clock frequency chosen should equal 16 times the required baud rate. Thus, for a baud rate of 1200, the clock frequency should be equal to $1200 \times 16 = 19\,200$ Hz.

Taking the the transmit operation first, the parallel data input is loaded into a buffer when the control line TBRL (Transmitter BuffeR Load) is taken low. As this data is loaded into the buffer, the fact that the buffer is now in use is indicated to the transmitting device by the output control line TBRE (Transmitter BuffeR Empty) going low. The data in the buffer will then be transferred to the transmitter register, the fact of the register now being in use being signalled by the second output control line TRE (Transmitter Register Empty) going low. Finally the data in the transmitter register will be passed to the multiplexer, to be supplied with the start, stop and parity bits, before the whole data packet is serially shifted out on to the line through the TRO (Transmitter Register Output) pin. All of this is under the control of a clock that, as stated before, will also set the baud rate for the transmission.

The receive operation is as follows. The serial data in arrives on RRI (Receiver Register Input). The baud rate can be different on receive from transmit. There is, therefore, a separate clock (Receive Clock) and, as before, the clock frequency is 16 times the required baud rate. The data packet received is loaded into the receive register, via the multiplexer, and when the Data Ready (DR) line goes high the parity and format are checked. The data word is then passed to the tri-state outputs via the receive buffer, where it can be read by the CPU. Once this has been done, the CPU causes the Data Ready Reset to go low, which clears the Data Ready line. The UART is now able to accept another serial word from the line.

Three types of error can be detected:

(a) Assuming that parity is in use, a parity error will result in the PE (Parity Error) pin going high, this pin staying high until the next valid character is received.
(b) A *framing error* occurs when the expected stop bit is not received. The FE (Framing Error) pin will then go high and remain in this state until the next complete character's stop bit is received.
(c) An *overrun error* occurs when a character is transferred to the receiver buffer register

before the previous character has been fully read. The corresponding flag for this error is the state of pin OE (Overrun Error) which goes high to signal the error.

The fact that each of the above types of error is flagged at an external pin of the 6402 allows the system designer to initiate an error correction procedure, such as the re-transmission of the character that caused the error.

There are two ways in which a UART can be used, known as the unconditional and handshaking modes. In the case of the former, the idea is that any time a character arrives it is immediately handled. This is simple but carries the reservation that the rate at which such characters arrive must be limited according to the selected baud rate. In the handshaking mode the UART decides, by means of control signals, just when it will handle a character. When a UART is used as a serial interface to a VDU/keyboard the unconditional mode is usually the one employed.

The above somewhat abbreviated explanation should provide an insight into the complexities of the device. There is a dual version of the UART known as a DART (Dual Asynchronous Receiver/Transmitter).

The 6850 ACIA

This device implements the requirements of the standard EIA RS232C serial interface, which is discussed in Chapter Eight. The block diagram appears in Figure 6.4. It should be noted that the device pins can be defined in 'blocks' with specific functions and relations to the microprocessor buses.

The parallel data connection is made through the eight data pins D0–D7 inclusive. Two address bus lines are used for chip selection, these being identified as CS1 and $\overline{CS2}$; thus one of the selected address lines at logic 1 and one at logic 0 will enable the chip. A third address line determines the logic level on the pin RS and, together with the logic level on the R/$\overline{W}$ line, provides the four binary combinations that control the addressing of the internal registers, known as Control,

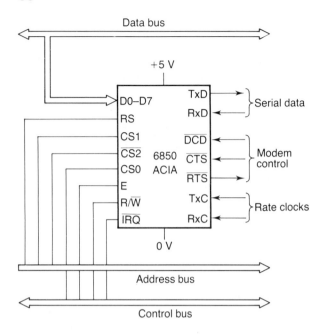

Figure 6.4 Block diagram of the 6850 ACIA interface IC

Status, Receive Data and Transmit Data, thus defining the mode of operation of the device.

Serial data in and out are via the pins RxD and TxD; these are TTL compatible signals, but they will invariably require external buffering to interface them to the serial devices. The modem-control lines control the interface in an RS232C modem link. There are two clocks, one for receive and one for transmit and, as explained previously, they may be different for each direction, thus providing different baud rates.

The 8251A USART

This device, the block diagram for which appears in Figure 6.5, permits both synchronous and asynchronous serial data transmission. The latter method has been described already and it should be appreciated that the data can be sent at irregular intervals, since the presence of the start bit will always identify the beginning of new data. In the synchronous method, data is transmitted quite precisely and the precision of the timing means that the start and stop bits are not required. Instead the same system clock is supplied to both ends of the serial link by means of a separate track. Every data word has its own predetermined 'time slot' into which it fits precisely. Any gaps in the actual transmission are filled by *null words*. Synchronous systems are very fast but at the cost of greater complexity than asynchronous links.

Referring to the block diagram of Figure 6.5, certain connections and their related functions may be identified. For example, the pin marked $\overline{CS}$

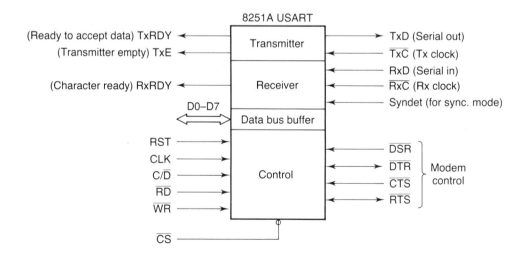

Figure 6.5 Block diagram of the 8251A USART IC

(Chip Select) must be taken low in order to select the USART. This happens when the appropriate address appears on the address bus and is decoded by external logic. The data bus, lines D0–D7, forms the parallel input/output path for the data. The two control pins, RD and WR, determine whether the data is being read from or written to the connected device. The pin C/$\overline{D}$ selects either Control or Data mode. This pin is usually connected to line A0 of the address bus. It functions in conjunction with the WR and RD lines as follows: when

C/$\overline{D}$ = 0 and WR = 0   data is transmitted
C/$\overline{D}$ = 0 and RD = 0   data is received

This is the *data mode*. When

C/$\overline{D}$ = 1 and WR = 0   control register is selected
C/$\overline{D}$ = 1 and RD = 0   status register is selected

This is the *control mode*.

The control mode is required because it is necessary to send 'set-up' words to the 8251A when the system is powered up. This is a common feature of other 'programmable' interfaces and the function of these set-up words is to establish the mode in which the 8251A USART will operate. Such options include: synchronous or asynchronous mode; read or write operation; word length and other parameters.

The pin marked RST is the reset pin. Taking this pin low will clear the selected modes and re-initialisation will be required. The pin marked CLK is, of course, the system clock connection. On the right-hand side of the IC block are the serial connections. TxD is the serial out pin (data being transmitted); RxD is the serial in pin (data being received). The corresponding transmit and receive clock connections can be seen as well. Finally, four pins for use with modems may also be identified.

The use of the 8251A USART as an interface between a CPU and the VDU/keyboard is illustrated in Figure 6.6. Another important peripheral interfacing device is shown in this case, namely the CRTC (Cathode Ray Tube Controller) IC. The latter is dealt with in detail in Chapter Seven.

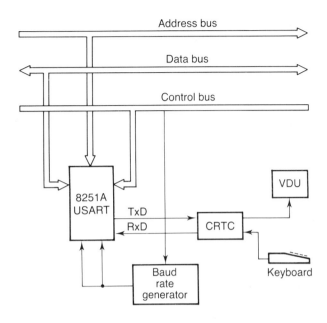

Figure 6.6 Using the 8251A USART IC as an interface between a CPU and VDU/keyboard unit

The SIO (Serial Input/Output Device)

A serial input/output controller IC is available for the Z80 CPU but it can, in fact, be used with a variety of other microprocessors. It provides two independent full-duplex channels with separate control and status lines for modems and other devices. The general facilities are much the same as those already specified for the 6402 UART in respect of the format of the data packet, that is, the number of data bits, start and stop bits, parity, etc. Data rates of up to 800 kbit/s are possible with a 4 MHz clock. The usual types of error can be detected and flagged.

PARALLEL DATA TRANSMISSION

Within the microcomputer itself, the data is transferred between CPU, memory and input/output ports on the data bus. By definition this is parallel data transmission. The foregoing discussion has considered a number of ICs that have been designed to interface the microcomputer to a device via a serial link. In cases where computer and peripheral are a significant distance apart, it makes good sense to make use of a serial link. However, since this method is inherently slow, it is preferable to use a parallel connection where possible. This is usually the case with printers, as is discussed in Chapter Eight in connection with the Centronics interface standard. Other parts of the system, disk-drive units for example, will also use parallel transmission. Apart from such specific applications, there are many more general cases where a parallel interface is of use. To implement this scheme, it is usual to include in the chip set of a microprocessor a parallel input/output IC for general interfacing use. Two examples of such ICs will now be discussed.

Parallel Input/Output

Parallel communication between a microcomputer and a peripheral takes place through a port in the Parallel Input/Output (PIO) chip. This is, in effect, a register in which data entering or leaving the computer is *latched* temporarily. In the case of common 8-bit devices, it is usual for the facility to be provided for the bits to be available as either inputs or outputs at will. For example, all the lines of a port may be set up to provide either an 8-bit input port or an 8-bit output port. Alternatively, the *bit mode* may be used in which any combination of individual input or output lines is possible. This is useful where it is required to accept single line data, from switches, for example, or to send out single line responses to indicators, such as LEDs, relays, etc. Some examples of the bit mode in use are shown in Figure 6.7.

While there are many CPU sets that could be considered, for the purposes of this discussion, the input/output devices relating to the well-known 6502 and Z80 processors will be used to illustrate the principles of parallel data handling. There are one or two noteworthy differences that will emerge.

The 6502 processor uses *memory-mapped port addresses*, that is, each register of a port has

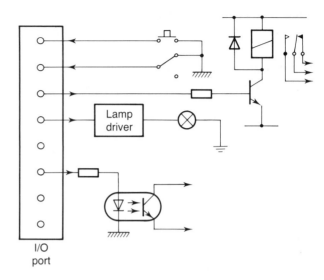

I/O
port

Figure 6.7 Using an input/output port in the bit mode

a unique memory address within the normal memory map for the computer and is treated in exactly the same way as any other memory location. Thus, the data transfers are effected by the use of the LDA and STA instructions, just as for the rest of memory, so that the instruction:

LDA   PORT A

loads the accumulator with the data held in the port A data register (this is an input data transfer) and:

STA   PORT A

stores the data in the accumulator at the port A data register (this is an output data transfer).

Any operation that can normally be performed on the contents of a memory location can also be performed on data in port registers.

Initialisation of the ports for a 6502 system, using the 6522 VIA chip, is effected by sending data to the data direction registers. On the basis that each bit of a data direction register has a one-to-one relationship with the corresponding bit of the associated data register, the direction of an input/output line is determined by the loading of either a binary 0 or a binary 1, as follows:

binary 0 programs a line as input
binary 1 programs a line as output

As an example, if it is required to set up port A so that its lowest four lines are inputs and the highest four lines are outputs, then the binary data to be loaded into the data direction register would be 1 1 1 1 0 0 0 0 which, in hexadecimal, is F0H.

By contrast, the Z80 uses a method of addressing the ports known as *accumulator input/output.* Each port is given a port address which is not on the memory map at all but is simply a unique number in the range 00H to FFH. It is actually possible to have port addresses in the range 0000H to FFFFH but, in practice, the 256 possible ports given by the 2-digit port numbers are usually more than adequate. To access these ports special instructions are available. These are as follows: to load data into the A register (accumulator) from port #2 the following instruction can be used:

IN   A,(02H)

Conversely, to send data from the A register to port #2 the following instruction would be used:

OUT   (02H),A

The dedicated input/output chip for use with the Z80 is known simply as the Z80 PIO. Its facilities will be described shortly but, for now, it is worth noting that the data used to initialise the directions of the port lines is the opposite to that for the 6502. That is,

a binary **0** establishes an **O**utput line, while

a binary **1** establishes an **I**nput line.

The Z80 PIO

This IC provides two 8-bit parallel input/output ports known as port A and port B, which can be programmed to operate in four different modes. Data entering or leaving the PIO is held in a Data Register (DR) and port operations are controlled by a Control Register (CR).

The modes are as follows:

Mode 0   As 8-bit output port, with hand-shaking.
Mode 1   As 8-bit input port, with handshaking.
Mode 2   As bi-directional port (Port A only), with handshaking.
Mode 3   In bit mode, all bits of either port can be programmed individually as inputs or outputs, no handshaking.

Interrupt facilities are also available.

To initialise the PIO it is necessary to write an initialisation program that establishes the following:

(a) The operating mode to be used.
(b) If bit mode is selected, which bits are to be inputs and which outputs.
(c) Whether interrupts are to be used or not.
(d) The interrupt conditions.
(e) The interrupt table address low byte, which forms the interrupt vector together with the contents of the Z80 I register.

It is necessary to be able to distinguish between words sent to the PIO as to whether they are command words or data. Pin 5 of the PIO is marked C/D for this reason, its logic level determining whether a command or data is intended, such that:

Logic 1 = Command   and   Logic 0 = Data

In a similar way pin 6 determines which port, A or B, is selected:

Logic 1 = Port A   and   Logic 0 = Port B

These logic levels can be determined by including these pins in the decoding logic, the simplest way of doing this being to connect one address line to each of these pins. Other address lines are decoded to select the PIO. The allocation could be as follows:

(a) The A/B select line is taken to A0.
(b) The C/D select line is taken to A1.
(c) The address lines A2–A7 are decoded to enable the PIO.
   The CE pin of the PIO is taken low by the decoding logic when the PIO is to be selected.

As an example consider the following:

(a) Any port address with A0 = 1 and A1 = 1 will select the function 'command word to port A', e.g. 03H, 07H, 0BH, etc.

(b) Any port address with A0 = 1 and A1 = 0 will select the function 'data to port A', e.g. 05H, 0DH, etc.

(c) Any port address with A0 = 0 and A1 = 1 will select the function 'command word to Port B', e.g. 02H, 06H, etc.

(d) Any port address with A0 = 0 and A1 = 0 will select the function 'data to Port B', e.g. 00H, 04H, etc.

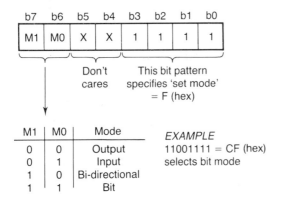

Figure 6.8 Structure of a command word for mode selection for the Z80 PIO

In the control word for mode selection, bits 0–3 are all 1s to identify that it is a control word, bits 4 and 5 are 'don't cares' and bits 6 and 7 determine the mode in accordance with Figure 6.8.

EXAMPLE

Initialise the PIO so that the following conditions are established: port A is input port, port B is in bit mode with bits 0–4 as inputs and bits 5–7 as outputs.

Solution

```
LD    A,4FH   ; code for input mode
OUT   (07H),A ; send to port A control register
LD    A,CFH   ; code for bit mode
OUT   (06H),A ; send to port B control register
LD    A,1FH   ; code for required bit pattern
OUT   (06H),A ; send to port B control register
```

INPUT/OUTPUT WITH A SIMPLE LATCH

Input/output devices such as the PIO just described owe their complexity to their built-in *programmability*. This feature is not always necessary and it is possible to employ a much simpler device to latch data in and out of the computer. The main limitation is that such a port will always be either just an input port or just an output port. The circuit diagram of Figure 6.9 uses the 74373 octal (that is, 8-bit) latch as such a port, of either type.

This IC has eight pins for the input data and eight corresponding pins for the outputs. All that is required to transfer data through the latch is to apply the correct logic levels to the pins marked CS and OE. The new data is released when CS is taken high and OE taken low. To drive these always with complementary logic levels requires only an inverter as shown. A logic 1 input to the inverter will update the latch; logic 0 to the inverter input will 'freeze' the data held.

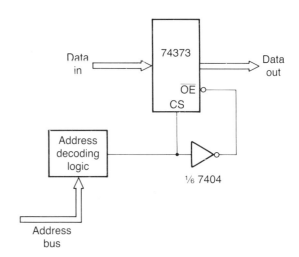

Figure 6.9 A simple dedicated port using an octal latch

EXAMINING DATA TRANSFERS

The inherent nature of microprocessor systems raises problems quite different from those encountered in the majority of analogue equipment. In the analogue case, the technician is usually able to examine the form of, and measure the amplitude of, the signal at various points in the signal chain using conventional test tools such as a CRO and an electronic voltmeter. When a program is running on a microcomputer, the logic levels on all lines of address, data and control buses are constantly changing. Why this is so is readily explained.

While the program is running, the address bus carries a changing binary pattern, corresponding to the regular accessing of memory locations. The data bus is similarly in a state of perpetual change as data bytes are transferred between processor, memory and input/output ports. There is a similar degree of activity on the control bus. For example, the read/write line alternates between its two states as data is fetched from, or loaded into, memory; clock signals control system timing; input/output requests are made, and so on.

A further complication is the speed at which these events take place, controlled by a clock oscillator operating, typically, in the range 1–12 MHz. Each event is, therefore, of extremely short duration. To examine such sequences, software *debugging* methods, such as *single-stepping*, can be used. However, such methods, by their very nature, do not operate in real time. What is needed is an instrument that can allow the microprocessor system to run at its normal speed, but which can 'capture' any portion of the program for detailed examination. The instrument that is capable of doing this is called the *logic analyser*.

LOGIC ANALYSER

A logic analyser is a multi-channel recording device that is able to follow the time behaviour of the system signals. Typically it will have 32 or more inputs that have to be attached to the data and address buses in order to capture the signals on these buses. This captured information is

stored in the machine's own buffer memory. The instrument operates at the full speed of the computer to which it is connected and so imposes no timing restraints on the computer's performance. Logic analysers may be totally independent instruments or may form part of a development system.

Connection to the test system is best accomplished by a custom-made 'pod', which picks up the required bus lines. It is possible to make the connections with a large number of individual spring connectors but this is an extremely tedious procedure, as one may imagine. In some cases, the CPU is removed from its socket, the test pod being inserted in its place; the CPU then plugs into the back of the pod, 'piggy-back' style.

The amount of data that can be captured is limited by the size of the analyser's memory. For a 32-channel machine, this may typically be 256 or 512 32-bit words. This will represent this number of consecutive states on the system buses. Exactly *which* states are captured is determined by separately made control connections, plus the appearance of a *trigger word*, which the analyser has been set up to recognise. This allows the program to run through the analyser in real time until the trigger word occurs. This initiates the capture of a block of data. At first it might be thought that the block of data captured in this way would always *follow* the trigger word. This is not necessarily so. It is possible to set the analyser so that the trigger word occurs at the beginning or end of the block, or indeed any number of words after the block's start.

What is the trigger word? It is a particular combination of, usually, events on the address and data buses that mark a point of interest in the program. For example, suppose that the following program line is the one that is to form the trigger word:

LD   (HL),A

Suppose that the address held in the HL register pair is 5D1A(H) and the data in the A register is 2D(H). When this data is to be written into the memory location specified, the address bus will have 5D1A on its 16 lines and the data bus

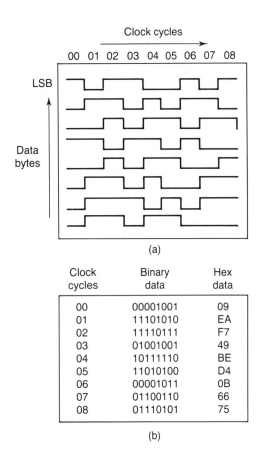

(a)

Clock cycles	Binary data	Hex data
00	00001001	09
01	11101010	EA
02	11110111	F7
03	01001001	49
04	10111110	BE
05	11010100	D4
06	00001011	0B
07	01100110	66
08	01110101	75

(b)

Figure 6.10 Comparison of the (a) time domain and (b) data domain types of logic analyser display

will carry 2D. Assuming that the analyser has been connected so that the address lines are more significant than the data lines, the trigger word will be 5D1A2D. When this particular set of signals appears on the analyser inputs, the data capture sequence will be initiated.

Once the data has been captured, it is available for examination. It has, therefore, to be presented in some way. The two principal methods are known as *time domain* and *data domain*. These are both shown in Figure 6.10.

The time domain display appears like that of a multi-channel CRO, with much compression in the *Y* direction. Not all channels need be displayed at once. A 'pip' may be used to identify the position of the trigger word, while a movable

cursor allows the data stream to be scrolled left or right.

One significant difference between the appearance of the time domain display of the logic analyser and a true CRO display is the way the former instrument 'doctors' the binary pulses so that they are all of regular form. In a sense, this type of display is idealised. It does not show the true shape of the pulses on the buses and should not be used for this type of analysis. The idealised waveforms are obtained by including, in the analyser inputs, a set of comparators. The latter establish whether the logic level is a 1 or a 0 and regenerate a standard level in either case.

In the data domain type of display, the data may be listed in binary and/or hexadecimal, often with line numbers. There are no hard and fast rules. The data presented consists of concurrent memory addresses with related data. The data will consist of the program opcodes or operands. It is possible to obtain a logic analyser that is able to disassemble the data and present it in mnemonic form as an assembler listing normally appears. This is, of course, a very powerful facility.

If the analyser is able to capture, say, 256 successive events, it is obviously impossible to display them on the analyser screen all at once. The area that is displayed at any instant can be thought of as a *window* on the captured data block (see Figure 6.11). This window may be moved along the block in either direction (hence the need for a cursor), with data being examined as it appears in the window.

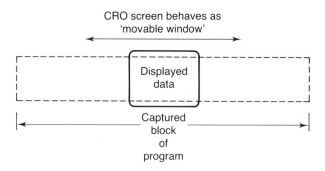

Figure 6.11 The analyser display forms a 'window' on the block of captured data

USE OF THE OSCILLOSCOPE (CRO)

It has been seen that the logic analyser is able to capture data from many simultaneous inputs; however, the waveforms that it displays in its time domain mode are not truly representative of the voltage transitions taking place. In contrast, while the CRO is limited in the amount of simultaneous information that it can display, a suitably chosen instrument will allow the accurate portrayal of such waveforms. Thus, the two instruments may be considered complementary, each having a role to which it is better suited.

Since the duration of microprocessor signals may be extremely short, the band-width of a CRO to examine them must be of the order of 50–100 MHz. Some laboratory oscilloscopes, with bandwidths limited to 10 MHz or so, will show greatly distorted versions of the system signals.

Given the right choice of instrument, the CRO can be used to check the waveform of critical signals. The system clock is one such, having well-defined rise and fall times that are specified by the maker of the CPU chip.

It is also possible to determine the presence or absence of specific activity on individual bus lines. Thus, a hardware fault that causes a single line to be 'stuck' high or low will show itself, as will a short circuit between adjacent lines. In the same way, loss of control signals, such as R/W, $\overline{CS}$, $\overline{IORQ}$, etc., can also be identified.

It is preferable if the signals presented to the input of the CRO are repetitive, since this makes it easy to synchronise their rate with that of the timebase. Apart from the system clock, other signals are less likely to be as regular or the recurring events are too widely spaced. A solution to this is to write a software loop that itself generates specific repetitive test patterns on the buses that can be checked with a CRO for predictable occurrences. Such routines may consist of transferring, between processor and memory, a short series of specially chosen numbers that causes predictable patterns on, for example, the data bus. Deviations from the expected pattern will provide clues as to the likely fault area.

Self-test Questions

6.1 For the 7-bit data word 1 0 1 1 0 1 1, what would be the parity bit for (a) even parity (b) odd parity? What is the main limitation of simple parity bit checking in error detection?

6.2 State *four* functions performed by a UART.

6.3 With reference to serial data transmission, explain the basic difference between asynchronous and synchronous modes of operation.

6.4 A 6402 UART is to transmit data at 2400 baud and receive it at 300 baud. Calculate the values of the clock frequencies for transmission and reception.

6.5 (a) Explain the role of start and stop bits in asynchronous serial data transfers.

(b) Draw the waveform of a '5 data bit plus parity' serial data package, conforming to the following format:

Data = 1 0 1 0 1   Parity = even   No. of stop bits = 1

6.6 With reference to parallel input/output, explain what is meant by bit mode.

6.7 Discuss the relative advantages and disadvantages of (a) the CRO and (b) the logic analyser for examining parallel data transfers.

SEVEN

Dedicated peripheral controllers

A general trend in the design of integrated circuits can be observed in the emergence of ICs which are virtually 'one-chip systems'. In the early years of integration, complex functions were usually assembled from large numbers of relatively simple ICs, resulting in rather crowded circuit boards. Nowadays, lifting the lid off a computer may well reveal little more than a handful of very large ICs, supported by a few smaller brethren. The technology behind this phenomenon is known as Large Scale Integration, or simply LSI. Whereas a 7400 quad 2-input NAND gate IC has less than 20 transistors integrated into its silicon structure, many modern LSI chips number such components in tens, or even hundreds, of thousands.

The result of this trend is the availability of a large number of special-purpose LSI ICs, that the circuit or system designer can call upon for providing certain essential, usually standard, functions. While each of these ICs may, therefore, be said to be *dedicated* to its chosen task, this often still leaves a useful degree of built-in flexibility, arising from both the hardware functions provided and the ability to be programmed into various modes of operation.

There are specific areas of application for such complex devices, which are common to most types of microcomputer. Examples are found in keyboards, displays and disk-drive units, for example. The aim of this chapter is to review a representative selection of these ICs. However, so that their contribution to the function of a complete computer can be more fully seen, the principles underlying each application area will be discussed first. This will be in sufficient detail to allow the reader a better insight into the design philosophy of each LSI device.

FLOPPY DISK SYSTEMS

Bulk storage of programs and data is essential to the operation of a microcomputer in any other than the most specialised of cases. In spite of its antiquity, a magnetic medium is still the usual choice for storage and is likely to remain so for well into the foreseeable future. The most significant development in this area seems to have been the ability to offer more and more storage capacity for less and less money. In this context, the *hard disk* or *Winchester* is becoming an increasingly attractive proposition. The alternative is the so-called *floppy disk*.

Floppy disks, also known sometimes as *diskettes*, are a relatively cheap and convenient mass storage medium for the microcomputer. They are often referred to as *backing store*, since they are additional to the storage provided internally by the RAM area of computer memory. Not only can the user employ floppy disks to store his own programs and data, but much commercial software, including a large amount in the public domain, is available in this medium also. The speed with which this data can be accessed is quite adequate for the majority of applications. The price of disks has reduced substantially during recent years, another factor in their favour.

If there is a problem with floppy disks it is the perennial one of standards. The original floppy disks were quite large, about 8 inches in diameter. This was followed by the size that itself became something of a standard, namely the 5¼″ so-called *mini-floppy*. These days hardly anyone mentions the larger size of disk, a very large number of users employ the 5¼″ standard, an increasingly large number of users now opt for the 'new standard' of 3½″, while a smaller (though still significant) number use the 3″ floppy disk. Software for the PC range of computers (originally an IBM machine but now cloned world-wide) is generally available on both the 5¼″ and 3½″ disks. Indeed, some PCs have both sizes of drive unit fitted so that either disk can be accepted. There are also ways in which data can be transferred between the two standards. The capacity of the 3½″ disk is comparable to that of the larger size, having up to 1 megabyte of total storage on the two sides. The smaller disk is more robust, being protected in a hard plastic sleeve, unlike the thin card sleeve of the larger disk. The price has also fallen to a comparable level.

Irrespective of the size of disk considered, the principle is the same. The disk itself is made of a thin, flexible plastic, the surface of which is coated with a magnetic material in which the data is recorded by means of a read/write head that bears lightly on the surface. This disk, when it is being accessed in the drive unit, rotates within its protective sleeve at a speed of 300 rev/min. Cut out of this sleeve are two 'windows'. One of these is a radial slot that provides the required access to the magnetic surface for the read/write head; the other is a small index hole which provides a positional reference or datum point. In the case of the 5¼″ disks, these windows are permanently open, hence the need for a paper pocket into which the disk is placed when not in use. In the case of the smaller disks, these windows are

protected by spring-loaded metal shutters that open automatically when the disk is placed in the drive. The position of the index hole is identified by an optical device.

In the same way that audio and video cassettes can be protected from recording over by breaking out a tab, the absence or presence of which a sensor in the machine will detect, computer disks can be *write protected* either by a small patch placed over the write-protect notch at the side of the disk, in the case of 5¼″ disk, or by moving a small plastic slide, that opens or closes a small circular hole, in the case of the smaller disks.

Other variations in disks include whether they are *single* or *double density*. In all cases, the data is recorded in the form of concentric tracks, of which there are usually either 40 or 80. The outermost track is generally called track 0. The two sides of 3½″ and 5¼″ disks may be accessed by independent heads, so avoiding the necessity for turning the disk over in use. By contrast, most drives using the 3″ standard are single-sided, so that to access the alternative side, the disk must be physically removed from the drive, flipped over and re-inserted.

As already stated, the magnetic recording surface is divided into up to 80 concentric tracks. A further division is made, radially into segments, producing sectors each of which typically has a storage capacity of 256 bytes. Each of these sectors is identified by address information stored at their intersections. This sub-division of the surface into small, individual storage areas has no physical reality. It exists only because of the magnetic pattern 'imprinted' on the disk surface by a process known as *formatting*. A new disk has to be put through this process before being used for the first time. Thus, when it is then put into service, the magnetic pattern is recognised and the allotted positions of the sectors identified. This arrangement of tracks and sectors is illustrated in Figure 7.1.

A 5¼″ disk, formatted for 80 tracks per side, has a track packing density of 96 tracks per inch (TPI). Thus, only the outer area of the disk is actually used for the recording of data, otherwise the sectors near the centre of the disk would become

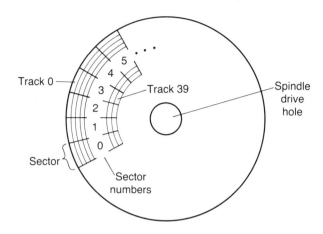

Figure 7.1 Arrangement of tracks and sectors on a typical floppy disk

unreasonably small and cramped. The two sides of a disk may be known as sides 0 and 1. Consecutively numbering *all* tracks on both sides of the disk would give the following arrangement:

Side 0   tracks 0 (outermost) to 79 (innermost)
Side 1   tracks 80 (innermost) to 159 (outermost)

A 5¼″ disk will be formatted to have either 40 or 80 tracks per side with 10 sectors per track. Each sector holds 256 bytes of data so that, with an 80 track, single-density recording, the total capacity will be: $256 \times 80 \times 10 \times 2 = 400$ kbytes. Using double-density recording the capacity becomes 800 kbytes, naturally.

FILES AND DIRECTORIES

Programs and data stored on disks are held in blocks whose size, in kbytes, depends upon the size of the program or data file. Each block has its own unique track/sector start address and a *filename*. The latter is usually restricted to a maximum of eight alphanumeric characters. The term *file* is, thus, quite general for any recorded block of data, regardless of its nature or function. To keep track of the names and locations, a *directory* is created on the disk, usually in the outermost tracks. This directory has a limited capacity, thus restricting the number of files that

can be held on disk, regardless of the capacity of the disk or the size of the individual files.

When a read operation is initiated for a specified file, the directory is first searched for a file of that name. If no such file exists in the directory an error message is displayed. If the file does exist, then the location and number of sectors comprising the file are read from the information held in the directory and the transfer begins.

When a write operation takes place, the new file is recorded at the next free sector onwards, and its name and other details are written into the directory.

It will be appreciated from the above brief discussion that the interface between computer and disk-drive unit has a complex task to perform, in reading/writing data to/from disk in a perfectly organised manner.

THE FLOPPY DISK-DRIVE UNIT

The drive houses both the mechanical functions and the electronics required to rotate the disk and access the data via the movable read/write head. The head assembly moves radially across the disk surface, actuated by a lead screw that is driven by a stepper motor. In this way the head is accurately positioned above the required track, while the sectors are identified, as the disk rotates, by their positions relative to the index hole mentioned previously. The position of the latter is sensed optically by a photocell. The basic form of a floppy disk-drive unit is shown in Figure 7.2.

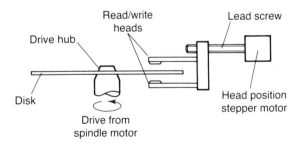

Figure 7.2 Simplified mechanical details of a floppy disk-drive unit

The drive electronics must perform a number of tasks.

(a) Move the head to the required track.
(b) Load the head and set up for either reading or writing.
(c) Generate or recognise various control signals, such as those that identify track 0 and the location of the index hole.
(d) Drive the spindle motor at an accurate rotational speed.

During a data transfer there are three identifiable operations, namely, head positioning, read/write control and data transfer.

As already stated the head is positioned by a stepper motor. This type of motor moves in specific increments of 'so many degrees' for each applied pulse. The program that controls this motor must, therefore, generate a specific number of pulses to make the stepper motor rotate through a particular angle. The lead screw converts this rotation into the required linear movement across the tracks of the disk to the one that has been selected. The head is then 'loaded' on to the disk, that is, it is lowered on to its surface. Once loaded, the track number is read to verify position, by comparison with the track register.

THE DISK-DRIVE INTERFACE

Interfacing a microprocessor to a disk-drive unit is performed by means of a special-purpose LSI chip known as a *Floppy Disk Controller (FDC)*. The schematic diagram for the Intel 8271 FDC IC, used in the BBC Model B microcomputer, is shown in Figure 7.3.

Software sends the required track and sector address to the controller IC. The IC then sets the head direction and head step signals so as to position the read/write head correctly. The pulse

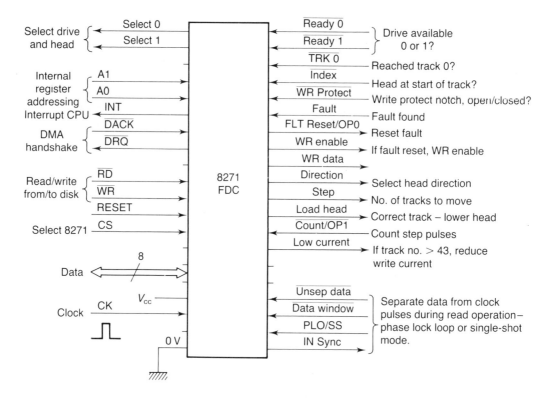

Figure 7.3   Schematic for the Intel 8271 floppy disk controller IC

generated by the index hole, referred to previously, is used to determine the correct angular excitation and from this, the required sector. When the head is correctly positioned at the required sector/track address, the head load signal is set and the head is then lowered on to the disk surface. The read/write signal determines the direction of data transfer. Data is, of course, written to, or read from, the disk in serial form, bit by bit. This means that the controller IC must also perform serial/parallel conversion (during the read operation) and parallel/serial conversion during the write operation. When the disk-drive is first switched on, the read/write head sets itself to the track 0 position; at this time, the track 0 signal is used to reset the IC's track register.

Other functions performed by the disk controller IC are the separation of recorded data from clock pulses, and error detection. In any serial data path, such as that between memory and disk-drive, there is always the possibility of data being *corrupted*, that is, one or more bits inverting their binary values. Clearly the received data will then be incorrect but, unless this fact is detected in some way, could be accepted as being valid. Writing to disk is normally error checked by reading during the next revolution of the disk. After, say, ten such attempts have failed to produce valid data, an error message should be displayed that may even identify the faulty sector.

Errors may be caused by electrical noise that, if temporary, will eventually allow a successful transfer; this is known as a *soft error*. Hard errors are usually permanent and may be caused by physical contamination of the disk surface. Error checking is usually performed by a sophisticated checksum method known as the Cyclic Redundancy Check (CRC).

There are essentially two ways of transferring data between the computer memory and the disk-drive unit.

One way is to use normal input/output techniques, the transfers, byte by byte, being handled by a software program. The A register or accumulator is used as the transit area for the data being transferred. The transfers themselves are initiated by interrupts, as is common also for other types of peripheral. This method tends to be slow because of the numbers of instructions that have to be executed during transfers of substantial amounts of data.

The alternative method is essentially hardware-oriented. It is either performed by the CPU itself or implemented in the form of a further LSI device known as a *Direct Memory Access Controller* (DMAC). As the name implies, this device permits a peripheral, in this case the disk-drive unit, to have direct access to computer memory without the need for the software involved in accumulator input/output transfers. There is more than one way of performing the DMA operation.

The easiest to visualise is when the DMAC issues a Hold ReQuest (HRQ) instruction to the CPU; the latter completes its current instruction and acknowledges with a Hold ACKnowledge (HACK) response. It then puts its bus connections (which are tri-state devices) into the high impedance state and goes to sleep as it were, only being re-activated to its previous task when the DMA operation is over. This process is called *floating the buses*. The CPU is provided with two pins designated Hold and HoldA for the purposes described. These correspond to the HRQ and HACK terminals of the DMAC, respectively. This type of DMA operation is illustrated in Figure 7.4.

This procedure is obviously not very efficient as far as the CPU is concerned. It has had to break off from its program to allow the peripheral device to take over. The latter is in fact 'hogging'

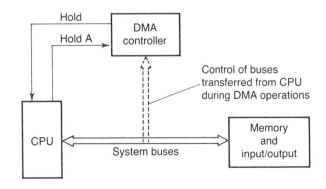

Figure 7.4 The principle of DMA transfers

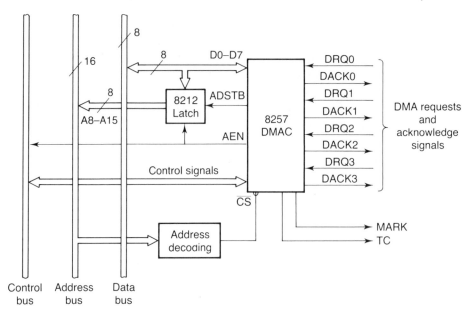

Figure 7.5 Intel's four-channel 8257 DMA controller

the address and data buses and system memory, and it is pertinent to ask whether there is some way in which they can be shared. The answer is yes, by means of a technique known as *cycle stealing*.

The DMAC and CPU now both function simultaneously, though slower than they would do if they worked entirely individually. When a clash for access to memory does occur, the DMAC assumes priority. All that the CPU does is to hesitate momentarily, as it waits its turn. For effective time-sharing between CPU and DMA device, the speed of the DMA channel is limited (as was implied above), otherwise the CPU would get no chance to run its program at all!

There is another way in which the DMA operation may differ. One type of controller may act merely in a supervisory role, taking no direct part in the transfer of data. Its function is merely to control the transfer process. In the other type the DMAC is connected to the system address and data buses in such a way that it performs successive read and write operations on the

data. The latter is actually transferred *through* the controller.

An essential feature of a DMAC is that it contains address registers, into which the source and destination addresses for the data are loaded, as well as a *byte count register*, which holds the number of bytes to be transferred. When data is transferred, it is done in blocks of a specific size, under the control of the last named register. Each time that the byte count register reaches zero, transfers momentarily cease while the above-mentioned DMAC registers are re-initialised. The DMAC will also be provided with information on the direction of data transfer (whether read or write), as well as the peripheral device address.

Intel's 8257 DMA controller (see Figure 7.5) provides four channels, each able to handle one peripheral. Only one channel can be active at any time. This type of controller causes the CPU to suspend its operations for as long as is needed to complete the data transfers. An application of this device is shown later in the chapter, when it is used in conjunction with another LSI device, a CRT controller.

HARD DISK SYSTEMS

Hard disks, also known as Winchesters, are of rigid construction, hence the name. The disks are usually made from aluminium, coated with a magnetic material such as ferric oxide or chromium oxide. The special aerodynamically shaped head is known as a flying head, and fly heights of 0.5–3.0 microns are usual. The heads can be designed to take off from, and land on, the disk surface, this feature being characteristic of Winchester drives. The disk surface is lubricated to minimise the risk of damage. The complete system is hermetically sealed to provide a totally dust-free environment.

Unlike the floppy disk, which is only rotated during access times, the hard disk assembly rotates continuously, at a speed of 3600 rev/min. Because of their bulk and consequent inertia, it can take anything up to a minute for hard disks to reach their full operating speed.

Hard disk systems may use either fixed or moving heads. Fixed head disks have one read/write head per track, an extravagance that is compensated for by the much reduced access time and the saving made by not requiring a positional motor drive. A moving head assembly uses one read/write head per disk surface, thus requiring a positional motor for accessing the required track on a surface, in exactly the same manner as for floppy disk systems.

Advantages of hard disks over floppies are:

(a) A much greater storage capacity. A 20 Mbyte system is now considered quite modest while, for those who can afford them, hard disk units offering in excess of 180 Mbytes are now available.
(b) A faster access time, by a factor of $10:1$, compared with floppy disks.
(c) System software is automatically loaded when the system is switched on, giving immediate access to application software such as wordprocessors, spreadsheets and databases.

Naturally, there are different sizes of hard disk, according to capacity, but the user may be less

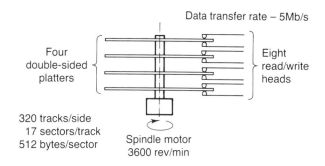

Figure 7.6 One possible arrangement of platters and heads in a hard disk assembly

aware of this since the hard disk unit is housed within the main computer casing. There is even a $5\frac{1}{4}''$ standard, which is capable of giving a capacity of up to 40 Mbytes of storage. Large capacity Winchesters are of *multi-platter* construction. The 22 Mbyte disk assembly shown in Figure 7.6 has four double-sided platters, thus requiring eight read/write heads altogether. Each platter has 320 tracks per side with 17 sectors per track, each sector having a capacity of 512 bytes. Using this data, the calculation for the total storage capacity is:

$$\begin{aligned} \text{Total capacity in kbytes} &= 8 \times 320 \times 17 \times 0.5 \\ &= 21\,760 \text{ kbytes} \\ &= 22 \text{ Mbytes} \\ &\quad (\text{approximately}) \end{aligned}$$

where 512 bytes = 0.5 kbytes.

There is a standard connector interface for Winchesters, the details being given in Figure 7.7.

KEYBOARDS AND KEYBOARD INTERFACES

There is a variety of devices that allow the user to input data directly into the computer. Of these the keyboard is the most familiar. Other devices, such as the mouse, trackerball, graphics tablet, etc., play their own roles in communicating with the computer.

The complexity of a keyboard may vary between the spartan simplicity of a hexadecimal

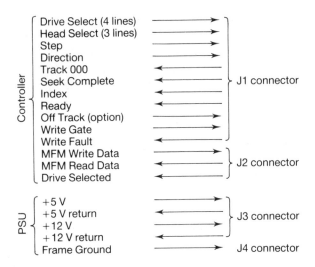

Figure 7.7 Connection details of the standard interface for Winchester (hard disk) drives

keypad (providing nothing more than the hexadecimal digits 0–9, A–F, plus a few control functions) and the luxury of a full typewriter-style keyboard. The latter may well have been expanded even further by the addition of a set of function keys and special control keys, according to the exact nature of the computer with which it is associated.

Keyboard Problems – Rollover and Lockout

It is virtually impossible to type without, at some time, pressing two or more keys in such rapid succession that they are almost instantaneous. Without some effective method of guarding against the consequences, this could result in the wrong codes being generated. Techniques that exist to prevent such errors include n-*key lockout*, *2-key rollover* and n-*key rollover*.

The simplest and cheapest is *n*-key lockout. In this method, the first key down generates a pulse known as a *keyboard strobe*. This causes the code for that key to be fetched. During this period any other keys down are totally ignored. The obvious disadvantage is that there are likely to be a number of missed keys, since one key must be fully released before the next is depressed.

In 2-key rollover, any key down will generate a keyboard strobe; a delay is then introduced for any further keyboard strobe until the first key has been released. The second key down will then be accepted. This is a method that works well as long as no more than two keys are down at a time.

The *n*-key rollover method is generally considered to be a luxury without much merit because of the complexity of the hardware. In use, any number of keys down will immediately generate the required codes for those keys, in the sequence of the keypresses.

The Keyboard Matrix

The electrical pattern beneath a keyboard is usually in the form of a matrix of conductors, consisting of m columns by n rows; this matrix is not necessarily physically similar to the keyboard layout. The keyswitches are each wired across a column–row intersection. Thus, an 8-column by 8-row matrix will accommodate up to 64 keyswitches. The use of such a matrix offers the possibility of a system in which the columns (say) are the input lines and the rows are the output lines. If no key is held down, then there is no conducting path between any of the columns and any of the rows. Naturally, a key down will then provide such a path. Every path is unique and is, therefore, potentially capable of identifying which key is down at any time. An obvious problem in this respect is that an input on any of the n rows could have originated from any one of the m columns. Some means must be found of making each column identify itself when a keypress occurs. A method of doing this, shortly to be described, is called *scanning the keyboard*.

Non-encoded and Encoded Keyboards

All keyboards will fall into one of the two above categories, though most will occupy the latter one. In a non-encoded keyboard, the process of scanning, and subsequent key identification, is largely software oriented. In the encoded type of keyboard, the accent is on the hardware.

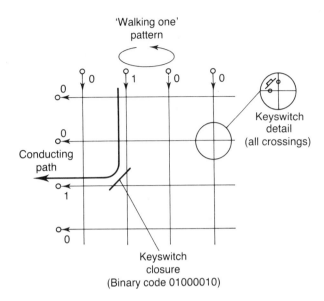

Figure 7.8 Scanning a 16-key keypad (4 × 4 matrix)

Taking the example of a simple 16-key keypad, this would be organised as a 4 × 4 matrix, as shown in Figure 7.8. To scan it, a 4-bit binary pattern, in which a single logic 1 is constantly circulated through the pattern, is applied to the four column wires. Thus, each of these wires is energised in turn by the logic 1, all others at this instant being at logic 0. Such a binary pattern is easily generated by software and sent to the column wires via four lines of the computer's input/output port, dedicated for this purpose. The successive states of the four column lines will be, starting with 1 0 0 0, next 0 1 0 0, 0 0 1 0, 0 0 0 1, 1 0 0 0, and so on, the sequence repeating indefinitely. The result of scanning the columns in this way is that, when a key is down in the column which is at logic 1, this logic level will be passed out through the appropriate row line. Since the scanning rate greatly exceeds the speed at which even the fastest typist can press successive keys, there is no chance of the keypress being missed.

A moment's thought should show that the key down has now been effectively identified. Each of the four column patterns listed above can form a possible combination with each of the four rows in which a keypress can occur. This gives the 16

unique combinations or codes required for the 16 keys of the keypad. For example, the code 0 1 0 0 0 0 1 0 (reading columns top to bottom; rows left to right) identifies the key that is in the second column in, third row down, as the one that has been pressed. The software must be written so as to include the following features:

(a) to identify when there is a 1 in the second half of the number (the row bits), since a 1 only exists here when a key is down;

(b) to read the complete number so as to check it against a table of such numbers held in memory, and thus identify the key pressed.

The program must continually be checking for the 1 on the row lines, as described, and this will correspond to the action of the keyboard strobe pulse (see later). On finding the logic 1, the program will then jump to a routine that checks the whole number as described in (b) above. This idea, in which a logic 1 is used to scan the keyboard lines, is known by the rather picturesque title of *a walking ones decode*.

In the alternative approach shown in Figure 7.9, the walking one pattern is generated by a piece of hardware. The ring counter shown is one of several possibilities. This is actually a type of shift register, consisting of a string of clocked D-type flip-flops in which the Q output of the final flip-flop is fed back to the D input of the first. Thus, any data 'in the ring' is constant and circulates continuously at the clock rate. It is arranged that only one flip-flop is set; therefore, the constantly circulating data consists of a single 1 and $n - 1$ zeros (where n is the number of stages of the register).

In the case of a 64-key keyboard, the matrix would be organised as an 8 × 8 layout – 8 columns and 8 rows. A scan pattern on the columns and rows could be generated by an 8-stage ring counter for the columns and a *1-of-8 selector* for the rows. However, there is an important point here; either the columns ring counter must be clocked at eight times the rate at which the 1-of-8 selector is clocked, or vice versa. For example, if the columns are clocked at a frequency f, then the rows could be clocked at

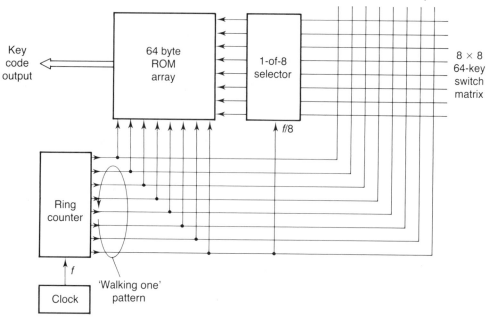

Figure 7.9 Using a ring counter to generate a walking one pattern for keyboard scanning

a frequency *f*/8. In this way, a row is held selected during the time that the *walking one* energises each column in turn. Then the next row is selected while all the columns are energised again. In this way all keys are scanned in a logical pattern, row by row.

The codes for each of the keys in the matrix are contained in a ROM, which is also organised on an 8 × 8 basis. It is virtually a carbon copy of the key matrix in this example, the spatial arrangement of memory locations where the key codes are stored following the layout of the matrix. The coincidence of row and column obtained by a keypress generates a logic 1 on similar lines addressing the ROM locations. As a result, an 8-bit code is output from the ROM, from where it will be passed to the CPU.

ASCII CODE

In theory, a variety of coding systems could be devised to encode the keys of the keyboard. In practice, there is one code in general use and a few others that may be encountered in certain

circumstances. The code most often used is termed ASCII, which is an acronym for American Standard Code for Information Interchange. This is generally regarded as a 7-bit binary code, though an 8-bit version also exists. This code is shown in tabular form in Appendix A and it will be seen that all alphanumeric characters, punctuation marks, other special characters and a variety of control characters are encoded in this code. Each is represented by a 2-digit hexadecimal number.

A scanning encoder is shown in Figure 7.10 in which the ASCII codes are generated directly by the keyboard matrix plus some extra logic. There is no ROM to store the codes in this case. Also included are two keys, of much value on computer keyboards in particular, namely SHIFT and CONTROL. Each of these, used in conjunction with other keys allows many more functions to be generated. The SHIFT key, of course, produces the capital letters plus those punctuation marks in superior positions on the key caps; it also has some special uses in application programs such as word-processors, as does the CONTROL key.

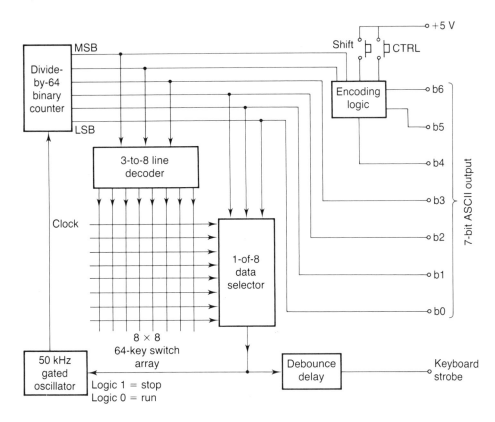

Figure 7.10 A 'ROM-less' scanning keyboard encoder in which ASCII codes are generated directly by the matrix plus extra logic

In this design an 8×8 keyboard matrix is addressed by the outputs of a 1-of-8 decoder (column scan) and a 1-of-8 data selector (row scan). The two logic circuits have 3-bit binary inputs provided from the 6-bit output of a *divide-by-64* binary counter. The decoder takes the least significant three bits of this counter and uses them to generate a walking one pattern on the columns. The data selector takes the most significant three bits and scans the rows for the appearance of a logic 1 (representing a keypress) at one-eighth of the frequency that the columns are being scanned. This essential frequency relationship between the two scanning rates arises naturally because of the binary division between successive stages of the binary counter. That is, the overall division ratio of the counter is 64, this being achieved because the circuit is, in effect, one *divide-by-8* counter (that for the

columns) followed by a second identical counter (that used for the rows).

The logic 1 output from the data selector, obtained when a keypress occurs, performs two functions. After a *debounce delay*, it is used as the keyboard strobe to inform the CPU that a keypress has been detected and that data is available. It is also used to inhibit the 50 kHz gated clock oscillator, thus preventing any further keypresses from having any effect while the current keyboard data is being accepted by the CPU, and so providing inherent 2-key rollover. This inhibit, of course, lasts only for as long as the key is down since, on the key being allowed to return to the normal position, the logic level on the inhibit line will return to logic 0 and the oscillator will restart. Relative to the speed that a human operator will depress and raise a key, the response of the CPU in detecting the keypress and accepting the data is extremely fast. There is, therefore, little chance of the keypress going undetected.

A STANDARD KEYBOARD ENCODER

The General Instrument AY-5-2376 Keyboard Encoder is an IC that has achieved some degree of acceptance as a standard basis for the design of

computer keyboards. This LSI device is a 2376-bit read-only memory that has the capability to encode single-pole, single-throw keyboard closures into a 9-bit code. The data and strobe outputs are directly compatible with TTL or MOS logic, thus obviating the need for any special interfacing. Among the features found on it are:

(a) Provision of external control for output polarity selection.

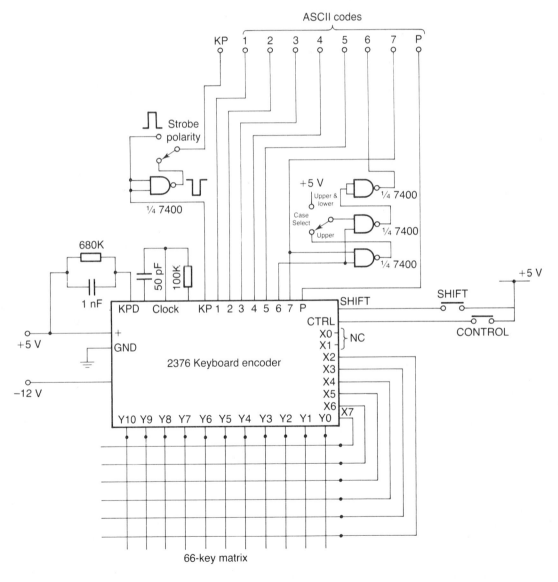

Figure 7.11   An application circuit for the 2376 keyboard encoder IC

(b) Provision of external control for selection of odd or even parity.

(c) Two-key rollover operation.

(d) *n*-key lockout.

(e) Externally controlled key debounce network.

(f) Internal oscillator circuit.

An application circuit for this IC is shown in Figure 7.11. As stated already, the 2376 encoder contains a ROM, which is organised as a 264 × 9-bit memory arranged into three 88-word by 9-bit groups. The SHIFT and CONTROL keys permit switching between the three 88-word groups. The 88 words themselves are addressed by the ring counters so that the actual address in the ROM that is accessed for data is formed from the 11 × 8 ring counter matrix with or without the SHIFT and/or CONTROL keys. This, in theory, provides for a total of 264 keyboard characters, but this is rarely taken up.

The maximum of 88 keys that can be used with this IC should be wired on an 11 × 8 key matrix with a single-pole, single-throw switch at each crossing. In the 'standby' state, with no keys pressed, the ring counters sequentially address the ROM locations, but the absence of a keyboard strobe pulse indicates that there is no valid data available.

When a key is depressed, a path is completed between one of the outputs of the 8-stage ring counter (X0–X7) and one of the inputs of the 11-bit comparator (Y0–Y10). Shortly after, the comparator sends a signal to the clock control and strobe output (via the delay network). The clock control stops the clocks to the ring counters and the data on the data outputs is now valid, as indicated by the strobe output. This data remains stable until the key is released.

THE 8279 PROGRAMMABLE KEYBOARD/DISPLAY INTERFACE

Space limitations preclude anything other than a brief mention of this versatile LSI device by Intel Corporation. It is a general-purpose programmable keyboard and display I/O interface for use with 8-bit CPUs.

The keyboard section can provide a scanned interface to a 64-key matrix. This section will alternatively interface to an array of sensors. Keyboard entries are strobed into an 8-character FIFO (First In First Out) register. If more than eight characters are entered an overrun status is set. Each keypress sets the interrupt output to the CPU. Thus, every time an input occurs the processor is automatically interrupted to service it. The interrupt service routine will normally read the contents of the FIFO register and send relevant data to the display (display RAM).

The display portion provides a scanned interface to various types of display, especially the 7-segment type. Display data is held in a small area of RAM which may be used as either 16 × 8 bits or dual 16 × 4 bits. The CPU can read or write to this RAM directly. Display formats possible are: right entry calculator or left entry typewriter.

Figure 7.12 shows the general application circuit, which can be easily modified for individual needs. The additional hardware is minimal, consisting of a 74LS138 3–8 line decoder which is driven from a scale-of-8 binary counter pattern obtained from pins SL0–SL2 of the 8279 itself. The eight output lines of the 74LS138 decoder, therefore, carry a walking one pattern which scans the keyboard matrix as described earlier. The return lines from the keyboard are input at pins R0–R7 of the 8279, where they load the FIFO register mentioned previously with specific keyboard codes (non-ASCII). The counter lines SL0–SL2 are supplemented by a higher order line SL3, these four lines then providing a scale-of-16 binary counter pattern as inputs to a 74LS154 4–16 line decoder which produces a walking zero pattern to multiplex a multi-digit display.

In order to initialise the 8279 for the various possible modes of operation, as well as to inform the device of the intended operation, such as read keyboard FIFO, write to display RAM, etc., it is necessary for the CPU to send specific control words. Full details of these appear in the maker's application notes, which all users are advised to consult.

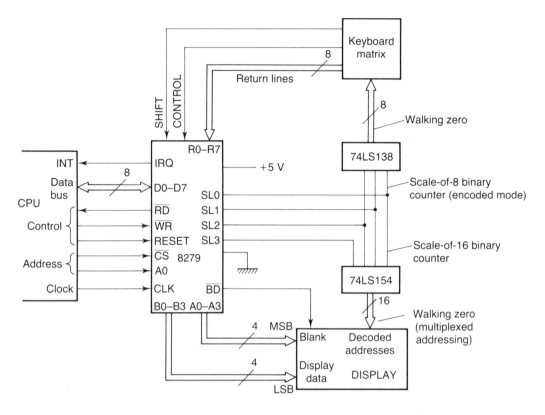

Figure 7.12   The general application circuit for the Intel 8279 keyboard/display interface

VISUAL DISPLAY SYSTEMS

Current display technology for microcomputers is, with the exception of lap-top machines which use LCD screens, based upon the familiar *raster scan* type of display employed in television receivers. This makes use of a cathode ray tube (CRT) with its associated electronics. A single picture is built up on the tube face by a scanning process, in which an electron beam is controlled so as to form a field and line structure (see Figure 7.13). By controlling the brightness (and colour) of the spot produced by the beam, the picture is created.

As shown in this figure, there are actually two sets of lines, each set comprising a *field*, the two fields being *interlaced* to form a picture. This process is repetitive, complete pictures being generated at the rate of 25 per second. Each successive picture will usually differ slightly from

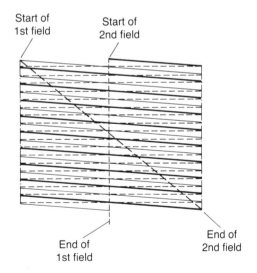

Figure 7.13 Scanning a CRT to form the line and field structure

its predecessor, this updated information being supplied in the transmitted signal. Thus, the effect of movement is obtained. This immediately highlights a difference between the 'origin of the data' for television and computing. As just stated, data is continuously received from the transmitter in the former case. The computer has no such source. The data used to produce the display is stored in an area of memory known as the *screen RAM*; it is stored in the form of ASCII-encoded characters. These will have been loaded into memory either directly from the keyboard or from an external storage device, such as a floppy disk-drive. One of the functions of the display electronics will be continuous reading of the screen RAM, so that the computer display is updated regularly.

Computer CRT displays do not always use interlaced scanning. Instead, the lines may be scanned, top to bottom, in a simple sequence. On completion of the scanning for one complete screen, the beam flies back from bottom right to top left to start a new scan.

The visible spot produced by the electron beam when it strikes the screen phosphor at high velocity represents the smallest possible element of picture information. For this reason it is known as a *picture element* or *pixel*, to use the jargon. Alphanumeric characters are formed from groups of pixels arranged in a matrix. These pixels are formed in an on/off manner by switching the beam current on or off at the appropriate time as the matrices are scanned in sequence. Figure 7.14 shows some examples of dot matrix characters, though they can be readily observed at first hand on the screen itself.

It should now be obvious that the display electronics has to perform a number of complex, mostly interrelated tasks. Such tasks include the production of the synchronising pulses for the line and field timebases to obtain a steady display; the generation of a suitable *serial dot* video signal; and continuous reading of the screen memory so as to *refresh* the display regularly. In addition, the ASCII codes read from this area of memory have to be converted to the corresponding dot patterns. This is done by accessing the row and column data for the characters, which is stored in a special ROM, known as a *character generator*. All of these functions, plus a number of others, can be carried out by a single LSI chip, known as a Cathode Ray Tube Controller (CRTC). This may be seen as the central feature of a typical VDU (see Figure 7.15).

The CRTC is able to communicate, in either direction, with the CPU via the data bus. It is provided with a high-speed clock, the frequency of which is determined by the rate at which the dot video output must be generated. Connections between the CRTC and the screen RAM and the character generator should be noted, in light of the foregoing discussion. The conversion of the parallel dot matrix information into the serial form of the dot video signal should also be noted. Other facilities that might be provided are a programmable cursor – block or underline, steady or blinking – and an input circuit for a light pen.

Examples of available CRTCs include the 8275 from Intel and Motorola's 6845. These differ in a number of respects, perhaps the most significant difference being the Intel chip's use of DMA to

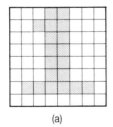 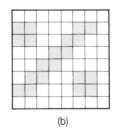 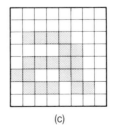

(a) (b) (c)

Figure 7.14 Examples of dot matrix characters

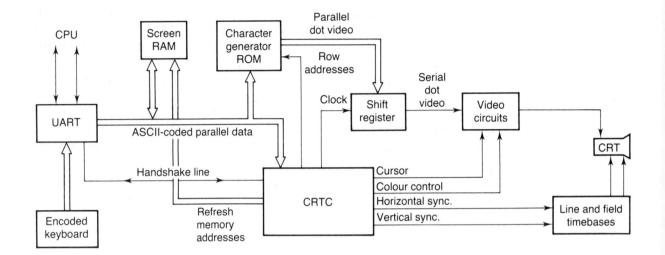

Figure 7.15 Block diagram of a typical VDU

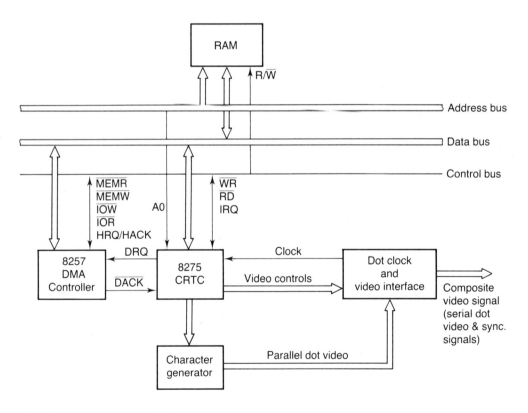

Figure 7.16 The Intel 8275 CRTC system

access the screen data, which is held in an area of the computer's main memory. An example of this IC in use is shown in the block diagram of Figure 7.16.

Five main blocks can be identified in this figure. The 8275 CRTC works in conjunction with an 8257 DMAC to access the screen RAM for the ASCII-encoded data. The latter is converted into dot matrix information by reference to the character generator; the outputs from the latter, plus video synchronising signals from the CRTC, are fed to a video interface block whose function is to generate the composite video output to the monitor. This composite video output comprises the dot serial video signal mixed with the vertical and horizontal display timing signals. The latter block includes the high-speed *dot clock*, whose output is fed to the CRTC.

The CRTC has two 80-byte row buffers, each capable of holding the dot pattern for *one row* only of a full screen-width of characters. One of these buffers holds the current row being written to; the second is filled with the dot pattern for the next row to be displayed. This operation of filling a row buffer commences when the CRTC sets the handshake line, DRQ, to the DMAC high; the latter responds by taking $\overline{DACK}$ low and then, using HRQ and HACK, as previously described, halts the CPU in order to access the screen RAM. The DMAC addresses the memory, and the data in memory is then loaded into the 80-byte row buffer in the CRTC.

Programming an IC of this type is complex, because of all the options offered. It is possible to have any number of characters per screen row between 1 and 80; the possible number of rows per screen lies between 1 and 64. The height of each character is also programmable. To control the operation of writing characters to the screen, CRTCs contain character, line and row counters.

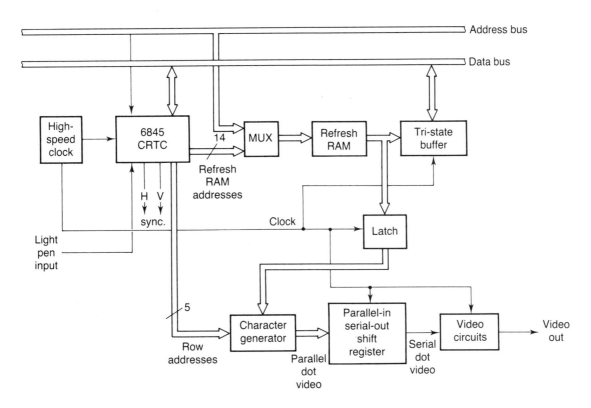

Figure 7.17 The Motorola 6845 CRTC system

By comparison, the 6845 CRTC does not use DMA to obtain access to memory. A separate area of memory, known as the *refresh RAM*, is addressed directly by the CRTC, using 14 refresh address lines. This permits 16 kbytes of refresh RAM to be addressed. A typical system using this particular CRTC is shown in Figure 7.17. Another feature to be noted is the provision of a light pen input. An external high-speed dot clock has to be provided. The CRTC outputs five raster address lines to access the contents of the ROM character generator. The parallel output of the latter is then converted into the required serial dot pattern by means of a shift register.

Self-test Questions

7.1 Discuss the effects that the development of LSI devices has had on the design of microprocessor-based systems.

7.2 Describe the way in which the surface of a floppy disk is organised for the storage of data. Why is such storage referred to as backing store?

7.3 List the main functions performed by the drive electronics of a floppy disk drive unit.

7.4 What are the two alternative ways in which data can be transferred between computer memory and a floppy disk unit? Discuss the relative merits of the two methods.

7.5 What advantages do hard disk systems have over floppy disk units?

7.6 (a) What is the difference between an encoded and a non-encoded keyboard?

(b) Explain the method of keypress identification that uses a scanning technique.

(c) How are keypresses used to generate ASCII-coded data?

7.7 What is meant by *pixels* and how are they used to develop the characters on a CRT screen?

7.8 Draw a block diagram of a VDU and explain the role of the CRTC IC in such a system.

EIGHT

Standard bus systems

A microcomputer is an example of a *bus-oriented system*. This means that it is based upon a concept in which blocks with specific functions (e.g. MPU, memory, interfacing devices), are linked together by multi-conductor 'highways', known as *buses*. Each bus has a specific role in the operation of the system. The address bus, data bus and control bus are familiar examples in the context of microcomputers.

Computers may be classified according to certain characteristics. One such, frequently used, characteristic is the 'width' of the data bus. Width in this sense means the number of data lines comprising the bus. In the majority of cases the figure for this will be either eight or sixteen. Thus, one may talk of 8-bit or 16-bit micros.

Regarding the bus as a group of conductors with a common function, it is then possible to extend the idea to the interface between the computer and external devices. Thus, when a computer is connected to peripherals, this connection may be made by a bus of a particular type. It is obviously going to be of the utmost convenience if the variety of such buses is kept to a minimum. This will increase the compatibility between the computer and commercially available peripheral devices. Perhaps the best way to illustrate this point is to consider the wide range of printers that are available. If each had its own unique interface method, this would almost certainly cause both confusion and inconvenience. Changing a printer would also mean changing the interface. Fortunately, this situation has been avoided. For practical purposes, there are only two principal standards in general use

for connecting a computer to a printer. Both of these are discussed further on in this chapter.

Not only printers benefit from the use of a standard bus system. There are many applications, both industrial and commercial, where a standard interface is of the greatest value. One of these will now be discussed.

THE IEEE488 INTERFACE BUS

This bus system was developed originally by Hewlett-Packard and is, therefore, also sometimes referred to as the Hewlett-Packard Interface Bus (HPIB) or the General-Purpose Interface Bus (GPIB). It is used for the interconnection of computers with instruments of various types. Some of these may be programmable, for which purpose the bus is ideal. Examples of possible instruments are digital voltmeters, power supplies and signal generators.

There are three types of device that can be connected to this bus:

(a) A 'listener', which is able to receive data from other instruments. Examples of listeners are: printers, displays, programmable power supplies and programmable signal generators.
(b) A 'talker', which is able to send data to other instruments. Examples of talkers are: tape readers, digital voltmeters and frequency counters.

It is possible for some devices to fall within both categories. An example of such a device is a programmable voltmeter, since this receives the data required to program it, and then sends out the data relevant to the measured variable.

(c) A 'controller', the function of which is to determine who talks and who listens on the bus.

Format of the IEEE488 bus system

This interface bus uses 24 lines, which are grouped as follows:

(a) An 8-bit bi-directional data bus. These eight conductors are actually multiplexed to handle the eight bits of the data bus, as well as the low and high bytes of the address bus.

(b) Three handshake lines:

Data available	DAV
Not ready for data	NRFD
No data accepted	NDAC

(c) Five control lines:

Attention	ATN
Interface clear	IFC
Service request	SRQ
Remote enable	REN
End or identify	EOI

(d) The eight ground lines comprise a braided shield, a logic ground and six individual ground lines forming twisted conductor pairs with the signals DAV, NRFD, NDAC, IFC, SRQ and ATN.

This bus has the flexibility that permits a microcomputer to be connected to several test instruments to form an integrated test system. Some idea of this flexibility may be gauged from Figure 8.1 where several different devices are connected to the bus. Their functions under the above classifications may be identified from this diagram. The microcomputer itself can act in the roles of controller, talker or listener. The printer acts solely as a listener since, apart from hand-shaking signals, it *listens* to the data that it must print. The signal generator is a talker (generating signals for use elsewhere), while the digital voltmeter is both talker and listener. The latter statement is true because it *listens* to the instructions which program it and then *talks* back to the microcomputer with the measured values.

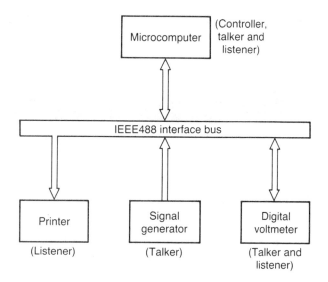

Figure 8.1 Example of the IEEE488 bus interface in use

From the hardware point of view, the system interconnections are often made between the devices by means of plug-in cards that connect to a *back plane* using 24-way connectors (see Figure 8.2).

Each of the devices connected to the IEEE488 bus has a unique address in the range 0–30, which may be selected by means of DIL switches mounted on the back plane. Associated with each device address are two other addresses, known as the *listen* and *talk addresses*. These are expressed in hexadecimal in contrast to the device address which is denary. The listen addresses start at 20H and go through to 3EH, while the corresponding

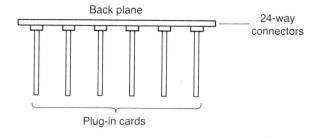

Figure 8.2 Physical arrangement of IEEE488 interface

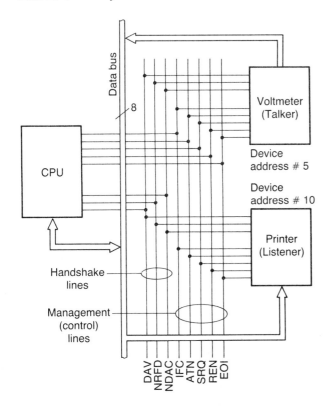

Figure 8.3 Establishing communication between a voltmeter and printer on an IEEE488 system

talk addresses occupy the range from 40H to 5EH. For instance, the first device addressed has device address 0; its listen and talk addresses are 20H and 40H respectively.

As an example, suppose the controlling device wishes to set up a link between a voltmeter (talker), with the device address 5, and a printer (listener), with the device address 10 (see Figure 8.3). To put the bus into the *command mode*, it would activate the line ATN. While holding this line in this state it would send the following codes via the data lines.

45H   talk address for device 5 (the voltmeter)
2AH   listen address for device 10 (the printer)

The controller would then release the line ATN and the dialogue between voltmeter and printer would commence.

Devices connected to the bus can signal the need for attention. To do this they use the control line SRQ to initiate what is in effect an *interrupt* procedure to the controller. The controller determines which device used SRQ by a polling method.

Finally, and very briefly, the remaining commands perform the following functions:

IFC   Initialises the system to an idle state, that is, no activity on the bus.

REN   Enables devices to respond to remote program control when addressed as listeners.

EOI   Indicates the last data byte of a sequence.

THE CENTRONICS 8-BIT PARALLEL PRINTER PORT

This standard derives from the interface originally used with a printer manufactured by the firm of the same name. Nowadays, the great majority of printers, especially of the dot matrix type, use this standard. The signals handled on the Centronics connector are: eight data bits plus handshaking signals. The latter are the Strobe (output from the microcomputer) and the Acknowledge or Busy signal (reply from the printer). The standard also specifies the type of connector, which is a 36-way Amphenol side-contact type. However, practical experience shows that other types of 36-way connector are also used, certainly at the point of connection to the microcomputer. The other pins on the connector are either ground pins or are not used at all.

SERIAL INTERFACES

It has previously been established that data may be transmitted either in a parallel format (as in the case of the Centronics port just discussed) or in a serial format. There are certain printers and electronic typewriters that make use of the serial connection. There are other devices, such as modems and VDUs that also use serial transmission. Several standards have evolved for use in such cases. One, with a number of derivatives, is of particular interest. It is known as RS232C. It is of American origin, but there is a near equivalent in Europe, known as V.24.

The RS232C serial interface

This particular standard establishes signal voltage levels and handshake signals for the communication of serial data in general. The acceptable voltage levels vary quite widely and are usually specified along the following lines: the 'one or mark' is defined as a voltage more negative than −3 V; the 'zero or space' is defined as a voltage greater than +3 V.

In practice, one might expect to find values of the order of ±10 V being used. The use of negative logic should be noted. The data is transmitted as an 8-bit group (7 data bits plus a parity bit), which is framed by a start bit (logic 0) and a stop bit (logic 1). This group will usually comprise a single ASCII-coded character. Between each character the line idles in the logic 1 state. The format of an RS232C character is shown in Figure 8.4.

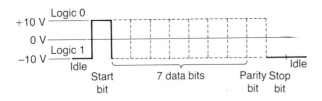

Figure 8.4 Format of a character transmitted using the RS232C standard

Such a logic system is obviously incompatible with TTL, and it is necessary to use interface ICs such as the MC1488 and MC1489A. A serial data link using the latter ICs is shown in Figure 8.5.

The speed of transmission is specified by what is termed the 'baud rate'. Loosely, and slightly inaccurately, this is understood to mean the number of bits per second. Thus, 600 baud may be assumed to mean data being transmitted at a rate of 600 bits per second. Examples of baud rates that have been used, or

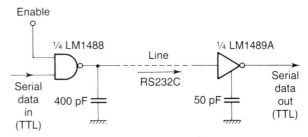

Figure 8.5 Using the 1488 and 1489A ICs to convert TTL levels to RS232C standard on a serial data link

are in use, are 110, 300, 600, 1200, 2400, 4800, 9600 and 19 200 baud.

The standard also specifies a 25-pin connector, with the functions of all pins defined. Most applications rarely need to take up more than a quarter or so of this allocation. Specifically, use may be made of the following pins:

Pin 2   Transmit data
Pin 3   Receive data
Pin 4   Request to send (RTS)
Pin 5   Clear to send (CTS)
Pin 7   Ground

RTS and CTS are the handshaking signals. RTS is a signal to a device which is to receive data; CTS is the device's response to this signal. For example, these handshaking signals may be used to pass data between two UARTs.

Figure 8.6 shows the use of an RS232C link to connect a computer to a VDU terminal. At the microcomputer end of the link (the transmitting end), a UART performs a conversion from parallel to serial data form. The serial data so formed is then transmitted over a link after conversion to the RS232C standard in a suitable interface. At the terminal (receiving) end the complementary re-conversion to TTL standard is carried out in a further interface. The data is still in serial form. Now it is passed to the second UART, which converts it back into parallel form before it is processed by the video circuitry. As it happens, the data is eventually converted to a serial form once more to drive the display. However, it is then no longer in ASCII code, but represents the pixel information for writing the text and/or graphics to the screen.

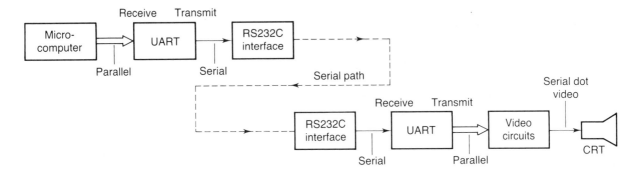

Figure 8.6 Connecting a computer to a VDU terminal with an RS232C serial link

The use of an RS232C interface is subject to certain limitations. The maximum data rate cannot exceed 20 kilobaud, and the line length is limited to a maximum length of about 16 metres at a typical baud rate. These limitations arise because the signal is single-ended (that is, one side is grounded) and is at high impedance.

A related, but improved, standard is the RS422, which uses a differential, low impedance signal. With this standard, data rates up to 10 megabaud are possible. At the same time, the line length limit is raised substantially to 1200 metres at 10^5 baud. The differential signal is developed by differential line drivers, such as the MC3847 IC, and it is sent on a twisted pair line. The MC3846 IC translates this differential signal at the receiving end to standard TTL levels (see Figure 8.7). Receivers of this type, being differential, bring with them the added bonus of being able to reject common-mode voltages. The latter are in-phase voltages, of equal magnitude, induced in the signal cable when the latter passes through a 'hostile environment'. This type of environment may arise because of the presence of conductors carrying heavy alternating currents, because of rotating machinery, switchgear, fluorescent lighting, etc., indeed anything that produces electromagnetic radiation.

Another enhancement of RS232C is RS423. The approach adopted in this case, to achieve high data rates and long transmission distances, is to use a low impedance, single-ended signal. The line is specified as standard 50 ohm coaxial cable. Maximum line length is about 1200 metres at 9000 baud. Line drivers (MC3488) and receivers (MC3486) are needed to interface to TTL standards. This interface is shown in Figure 8.8.

Figure 8.7 The balanced transmission path of the RS422 standard

Figure 8.8 The RS423 single-ended interface

Self-test Questions

8.1 Why is a computer known as a bus-oriented system?

8.2 Draw a block diagram in which a microcomputer controls three other devices through an IEEE488 interface. State what the controlled devices are and define their functions as:

(a) controller   (b) talker or   (c) listener.

8.3 What is the advantage of using a bus interface system such as IEEE488?

8.4 (a) Describe the serial interfacing system known as RS232C. Draw the waveform of a typical data word being transmitted to this standard.
(b) State two practical uses for the RS232C interface.

NINE

An interfacing case study

INTRODUCTION

The BTEC standard unit around which this book is largely based calls for students to carry out a case study of a microprocessor system, and to design and test both the hardware and software needed to implement the system. This section of the syllabus accounts for 50% of the total assessment. In spite of its obvious importance, it is logical that it should appear at the end of this book, since no case study of any value can be carried out until a sound understanding of the basic principles, and an awareness of available hardware, has been acquired. As for the nature of the case study, the precise choice is in the hands of the student concerned. A broad choice is offered between a commercial system and an industrial one. The aim of the case study is, of course, primarily to analyse the *interfacing* needs of a system.

While the actual choice of a subject for the case study will be a matter for the staff and students concerned, there is, however, the possibility of a unified approach that might be worthy of consideration. To give some guidance in the matter of both hardware and software design, a sample case will now be discussed in order to demonstrate a working procedure. While the choice lies between a commercial option (e.g. keyboard/VDU/CPU) and an industrial option (e.g. transducer/CPU/controller), it will serve both

cases if a choice from the latter option is made. Bearing in mind also the constraints of time allotted and hardware availability, a simple industrial system will often be the more feasible choice to implement.

A SAMPLE CASE STUDY: A MULTIPLEXED TEMPERATURE-MONITORING SYSTEM

The choice is quite arbitrary and is used only to illustrate the steps of the design process. The logical starting point is a written statement of the system requirements. This appears as follows.

1 Statement

It is required to monitor temperature at four points in a test environment. Data for these temperatures are required to be input at a port by a handshaking technique. It is expected that the temperatures will be in the range $+40\,°C$ to $+80\,°C$. The microcomputer will process the data in two ways:

(a) Compute the mean temperature and output it to a voltmeter. By appropriate scaling the voltmeter can be made to read temperature directly.
(b) If any of the individual temperatures exceeds a given value an LED (one for each input) will be lit.

2   Block diagram

The statement leads to a block diagram (probably via a few doodled attempts!). The block diagram of Figure 9.1 shows how the proposed system might look.

The four temperature transducers are shown connected to the inputs of a multiplexer. Since it is unlikely that the analogue voltages from the transducers will be large enough to drive a converter directly, an amplifier will be needed to raise the signal level. Because there is unlikely to be any major variation in the analogue voltages between individual transducers, only one amplifier, of fixed gain, will be needed. This statement is based on the implications of the original statement, namely that all four transducers operate in the same environment and in a limited temperature range.

The output of the signal amplifier drives an ADC; the binary output from the latter is connected to port A of the microcomputer. Here it will be read by the microcomputer program. Handshaking is effected by two lines, Start Convert and Status, between the ADC and a second port, port B. The latter port also provides:

(a) A scale-of-4 binary counter output to sequence the MUX block.

(b) Connections to four LED 'over temperature' indicators.

A third port, port C, is used for the voltmeter. The binary output, representing mean temperature, drives a DAC which in turn drives a voltmeter (analogue or digital).

3   Hardware requirements

The block diagram allows the hardware needs of the system to be identified. Choices can then be made from known, available devices. The items may be listed as follows:

(a) Four temperature transducers, suitable for measurement in the range 40–80 °C.

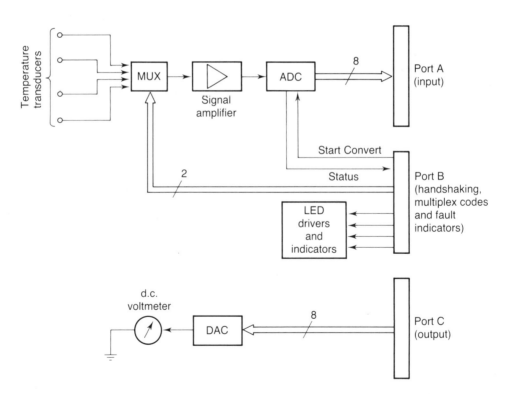

Figure 9.1   Block diagram of the proposed temperature monitoring system

(b) A 4-line to 1-line analogue multiplexer.

(c) A signal amplifier. Gain will be the criterion rather than bandwidth, since temperature is inherently a slowly changing quantity.

(d) An analogue-to-digital converter.

(e) A digital-to-analogue converter.

(f) LED indicators with drivers.

Taking (a) first, the choice of transducer will depend upon the temperature range, primarily. From Chapter Two, the following possibilities are determined:

(a) Copper–constantan thermocouples.

(b) LM35DZ temperature sensor ICs.

The thermocouple has a typical sensitivity of 50 μV/°C. For the temperature range quoted, namely +40 to +80°C, the signal voltage range is obtained from:

$$\text{Signal voltage range} = 50 \times 10^{-6} \times (80 - 40)$$
$$= 2 \text{ mV}$$

This is the *total change* of voltage over the whole range of the measured variable and implies a high gain requirement in the following amplifier.

By comparison, the LM35DZ sensor has a sensitivity figure of 10 mV/°C. For the same temperature range, we have:

$$\text{Signal voltage range} = 10^{-2} \times (80 - 40)$$
$$= 0.4 \text{ V}$$

This is clearly a much more usable voltage and indicates this device as the logical choice, assuming that there are no other factors (accuracy, linearity, stability, etc.) that have to be considered. For the purposes of this study it is assumed that there are no other factors to influence the choice. Consequently, LM35DZ sensors will be used.

It should be noted that the figure of 0.4 V is the *change* of signal voltage and not an absolute value. Assuming a linear relation between output voltage and temperature down to 0 °C, the actual voltages from the sensor ought to be:

0 V at 0 °C; +0.4 V at +40 °C; +0.8 V at +80 °C

This raises a particular problem. If the datum is taken as 0 °C, as might seem logical, the range from this datum to +40 °C will also produce a range of digital outputs from the ADC. Since this temperature range is not of interest, half of the available range of the converter will clearly be wasted. It would be better to suppress this range and make +40 °C the datum instead. Then the input range to the ADC will be the 0.4 V variation due to the temperature range from +40 °C to +80 °C. This can be usefully employed to generate the full range of codes from 00H to FFH. As has been discussed in Chapter Five, this will allow maximum resolution to be achieved.

The requirement for a 4-line to 1-line multiplexer is easily and cheaply met by using a 4052BE 2-pole 4-way analogue switch. Although this IC is a dual multiplexer, it is cheap enough to permit the spare half to be ignored. The system so far looks as in Figure 9.2, where the temperature sensors are shown connected to the multiplexer inputs and the channel select inputs are identified. Power supply connections are also shown.

The signal gain requirement can be met using a standard opamp such as the ubiquitous 741, wired as a non-inverting amplifier. A set zero control can be included so as to offset the analogue voltage at the datum temperature of +40 °C, as discussed above. The arrangement is shown in Figure 9.3.

At this point the actual gain of the amplifier is not known since the choice of a suitable ADC has not been made. Once this choice has been made, its input range requirements can be matched to the signal voltage available and the required gain calculated. This in turn will lead to a calculation of amplifier component values.

There are several possibilities, of which the ZN427E is as suitable as any. This has three handshaking lines, whose functions may be stated as follows:

The WR line, also known as Start Convert; a negative-going transition must be sent to the ADC on this line to begin a conversion cycle.

The Busy line, also known as Status; this line will be high during conversion but will go low when conversion is complete. The microprocessor will respond to this

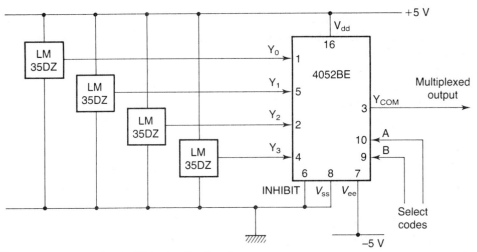

Figure 9.2 The arrangements for multiplexing the inputs

transition. It can be used to initiate an interrupt sequence or, as in this case, can be detected by a polling program.

The RD line, which is a Strobe, that is taken low by the microprocessor prior to reading the data at the input port. It enables the output from the ADC.

The ZN427E will accept an analogue input range of 0 to +5 V and will output an 8-bit binary output over this range. This allows the gain A_v of the signal amplifier to be calculated.

$$A_v = \frac{\text{Input voltage range of ADC}}{\text{Available signal voltage range}}$$

$$= \frac{5}{0.4}$$

$$= 12.5$$

It will be seen that the circuit of Figure 9.3 includes resistor values that will allow this gain figure to be obtained. A preset resistor permits precise setting of the gain to be carried out.

This completes the survey of hardware requirements for the input side of the system. The needs for the output side are readily assessed, as follows.

The LED indicators with drivers are shown in Figure 9.4. These are driven directly from lines PB4–7 inclusive on port B.

The DAC requirement can be met by the use of

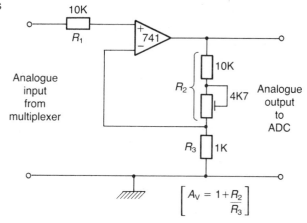

Figure 9.3 Arrangement of the signal amplifier

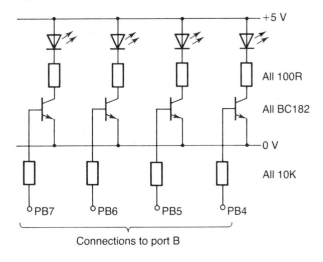

Connections to port B

Figure 9.4 LED indicators and drivers

a ZN428E, which is the complement of the ADC used, the ZN427E, by means of a ZN425E, wired in the DAC mode, among others. The choice in this case is the latter DAC as it avoids the need for a separate output line for strobing in the port data.

To reduce the hardware requirements on the provision of the three ports themselves, it is suggested that ports A and B are implemented in a Z80 PIO (assuming a Z80-based system) and port C is provided by an octal latch of the type shown in Figure 6.9.

4 Software requirements

The complete software to run the system can be described by the flowchart of Figure 9.5. It is recommended that a flowchart be drawn up as an aid to organising one's thoughts. It is better to think of the program, not as a long string of instructions, but as a series of *modules*, each of which performs its own specific function. By adopting a modular approach to programming, each module can be designed from a knowledge of its purpose and it can be linked to other, related, modules by appropriate calls and jumps, etc. Each block on a flowchart may be a separate module, but more often a module will consist of several blocks.

No attempt to write the actual software for the system will be made here. That is outside the scope of this particular book. However, a few hints may not come amiss.

(a) To generate the set of select codes for the MUX, i.e. 00–11 inclusive, start by clearing a register. Then INCrement it once for each successive conversion cycle. After each cycle, test for the 11 state (comparison instruction) and when found, reset the register to start again.

(b) The Start Convert pulse consists of a transition from 1 to 0, a short delay, and then a transition back to the logic 1 state. Before implementing this pulse, write a logic 1 to the Start Convert port line after the ports have been initialised. This may be considered as being within the first block of the flowchart

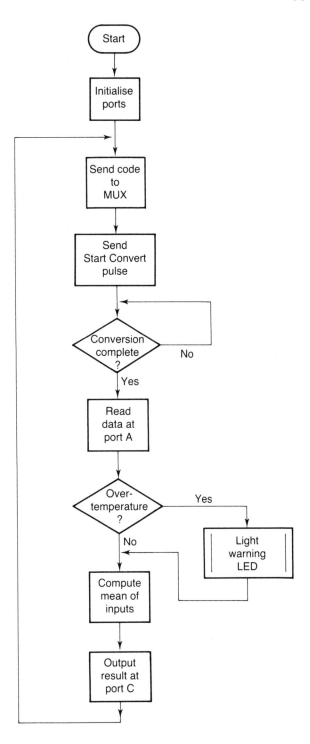

Figure 9.5 Flowchart for the system software

and ensures that a low level is not sent to the ADC before the MUX receives its select code. The pulse itself will then be generated by a 1-to-0 transition, a Call to a delay subroutine, followed by a 0-to-1 transition.

(c) The check for a completed conversion consists of testing the port line for Status for a logic 0. This can be done using instructions such as Bit or And, after loading the accumulator with the data from this port.

(d) Testing for over-temperature involves nothing more than comparing the value read in from port A with some agreed value. The comparison instruction will perform this function, the result setting or resetting a flag which the program then checks. On finding a result greater than the permitted value, a Jump is made to a suitable routine which sends a logic 1 level to one of the LEDs.

(e) The main program must add the values of the four successive inputs, one from each transducer in turn. A register must be set up as a counter to keep track of the accumulative addition involved. On completion of the addition, the result can be right-shifted *two* places to perform the required division-by-4 that yields the mean value. This is then output at port C where it is converted to an analogue quantity for reading by the voltmeter. If necessary, the program can be made to modify the result by some scaling factor to make the voltmeter direct reading.

Appendix A

ASCII CODE TABLE

HEX (LSD)	(MSD)	0	1	2	3	4	5	6	7
0		NUL	DLE	SPACE	0	@	P	`	p
1		SOH	DC1	!	1	A	Q	a	q
2		STX	DC2	"	2	B	R	b	r
3		ETX	DC3	#	3	C	S	c	s
4		EOT	DC4	$	4	D	T	d	t
5		ENQ	NAK	%	5	E	U	e	u
6		ACK	SYN	&	6	F	V	f	v
7		BEL	ETB	'	7	G	W	g	w
8		BS	CAN	(	8	H	X	h	x
9		HT	EM	)	9	I	Y	i	y
A		LF	SUB	*	:	J	Z	j	z
B		VT	ESC	+	;	K	[	k	{
C		FF	FS	,	<	L	\	l	
D		CR	GS	_	=	M	]	m	}
E		SO	RS	.	>	N	^	n	
F		SI	US	/	?	O		o	DEL

Example: reading the digits of the code in the order MSD,LSD, the ASCII code for A is 41.

Appendix B

ANSWERS TO NUMERICAL QUESTIONS

Chapter Two
2.3 (a) $K = 1.786$ (b) $E = 8 \times 10^{-3}$

Chapter Five
5.2 800 Hz (twice the signal frequency)
5.4 1.22 mV; 4095 quantisation intervals
5.5 (a) 1.95 mV (b) 0.0244%
5.8 2.55 ms and 80 μs respectively.

Chapter Six
6.1 (a) parity bit = 1 (b) parity bit = 0
6.4 Transmit clock = 38.4 kHz; receive clock = 4.8 kHz

BIBLIOGRAPHY

Wilkinson B. and Horrocks D. (1980) *Computer Peripherals*, London, Hodder & Stoughton.

Ferguson J. (1985) *Microprocessor Systems Engineering*, Wokingham, Addison-Wesley.

Holland R. C. (1984) *Microprocessors and their Interfacing*, Oxford, Pergamon Press.

Lesea A. and Zaks R. (1977) *Microprocessor Interfacing Techniques*, Berkeley CA, Sybex.

Hall D. (1980) *Microprocessors and Digital Systems*, Maidenhead, McGraw-Hill.

Potton A. (1983) *Microprocessor based Systems Level IV*, London, TEC/Hutchinson.

Morse M. J. (1982) *Microprocessor based Systems Level V*, London, TEC/Hutchinson.

Loveday G. (1984) *Practical Interface Circuits for Micros*, London, Pitman.

Index